5.00

BIOLOGICAL BASIS OF BEHAVIOR

A Program

PRENTICE-HALL INTERNATIONAL, INC., *London*
PRENTICE-HALL OF AUSTRALIA, PTY., LTD., *Sydney*
PRENTICE-HALL OF CANADA, LTD., *Toronto*
PRENTICE-HALL OF JAPAN, INC., *Tokyo*

BIOLOGICAL BASIS OF BEHAVIOR

A Program

F. J. McGUIGAN

Professor of Psychology
Hollins College, Virginia

PRENTICE-HALL, INC.
Englewood Cliffs, N. J.

Current printing (last digit):
13   12   11   10   9   8   7

C 07672

For RICHARD
"Mister Man"

TO THE STUDENT

In this course, you will learn about the general physiological principles that underlie that part of nature that is of greatest interest to us all—human behavior. The goal is to better understand what goes on within us when we behave. More particularly, you will see how objects and events around you cause your sense mechanisms to send "messages" through your nervous systems, and finally to your muscles so that you can act.

In order to facilitate your learning, this course is programed for you. As education goes, programed learning is a new approach. To date, the results of programed learning have been extremely encouraging. One of its main ideas is that it breaks material into small pieces so that it is easy to handle. The small portions are quickly and easily learned and before you know it they all add up and you will find that you have learned a great deal.

The procedure is simple. First, cover the answers on the left-hand side of the page with the slider provided. Second, read item (frame) number one. Third, write the missing word in frame number one, and finally, move the slider down the page *just enough so that you see the answer to the first (and only the first) frame.* Then go through the rest of the frames in the program the same way.

A few cautions:

1. Do each item in its proper turn—do not skip a frame.
2. Avoid careless answers—think about what you write in each blank and try to connect your answer with the idea in each frame.
3. Make sure that you actually write out each answer.
4. Do not look ahead—it is very important that you *look at each answer only after you have written it in the corresponding item.* If you do look ahead, you will only be fooling yourself, and your learning will be retarded.
5. You should study the figures in detail, for they contain a large amount of valuable information. In order to help cement your learning, you will be asked at various places to draw the figures for yourself. In such cases, use any available 8½ x 11 paper.
6. In several frames, you might write in a word that means the same as the answer. Where you have written in a synonym for the answer, you should regard your word as correct.

This program has been thoroughly tested with a large number of students in several different kinds of biology and psychology classes. Without exception, the results showed that the classes not only learned a considerable amount, but also preferred this program to reading a book.

Now go ahead—you should not only profit from this course, but also enjoy it.

ACKNOWLEDGMENT

The author is truly grateful to the many students and colleagues who so generously gave of their time and talent in the development of this program. Unfortunately, space does not permit the naming of all these individuals; however, special thanks is extended to Allen Calvin, Vincent Dethier, Edward Green, and Robert Silverman for their professional comments, and to Linda Devin and Adelaide Johnston who offered extremely thorough and valuable criticism. Thanks, too, to Richard Popp who assisted in ways too numerous to specify, and to Charlotte Collings for her expert secretarial performance. Finally, the author wishes to acknowledge his great indebtedness and sincere appreciation to Hollins College for providing the stimulating atmosphere in which he worked.

F. J. McGUIGAN

CONTENTS

xiii

THE NERVOUS SYSTEMS

EFFECTORS

BIOLOGICAL BASIS
OF BEHAVIOR

A Program

Pronunciation Key

The symbol (′), as in **moth·er** (mŭ<u>th</u>′ər), is used to mark primary stress; the syllable preceding it is pronounced with greater prominence than the other syllables in the word. The symbol (′), as in **grand·moth·er** (grănd′mŭ<u>th</u>′ər), is used to mark secondary stress; a syllable marked for secondary stress is pronounced with less prominence than the one marked (′) but with more prominence than those bearing no stress mark at all.

ă	act, bat	m	my, him	ŭ	up, love
ā	able, cape	n	now, on	ū	use, cute
â	air, dare	ng	sing, England	û	urge, burn
ä	art, calm				
b	back, rub	ŏ	box, hot	v	voice, live
ch	chief, beach	ō	over, no	w	west, away
d	do, bed	ô	order, ball	y	yes, young
		oi	oil, joy	z	zeal, lazy, those
ĕ	ebb, set	o͝o	book, put	zh	vision, measure
ē	equal, bee	o͞o	ooze, rule		
f	fit, puff	ou	out, loud	ə	occurs only in un-
g	give, beg				accented syllables
h	hit, hear	p	page, stop		and indicates the
ĭ	if, big	r	read, cry		sound of
ī	ice, bite	s	see, miss		a *in* alone
		sh	shoe, push		e *in* system
j	just, edge	t	ten, bit		i *in* easily
k	kept, make	th	thin, path		o *in* gallop
l	low, all	<u>th</u>	that, other		u *in* circus

Reprinted from THE AMERICAN COLLEGE DICTIONARY (Copyright 1947, © Copyright 1962) by permission of Random House, Inc.

INTRODUCTION

Section I: Overview

organism 1. Scientists are interested in studying all organisms. A dog is an organism, a chimpanzee is an organism, and a man is an _____.

species 2. A SPECIES (pronounced spē'shĭz) is a group of organisms that have certain characteristics in common. There are many different _____ of organisms in the world.

organisms 3. These species range from very simple one-celled organisms to highly complex multi-celled _____.

organisms 4. The species called *Paramecium caudatum* is composed of a group of one-celled _____ that have certain characteristics in common.

species 5. Men are organisms that belong to the_____ called *Homo sapiens*.

species 6. *Homo sapiens* is a _____ that is made
organisms up of highly complex multi-celled _____
characteristics that have certain _____ in common.

behavior 7. Clearly all sciences differ in some respects. But a number of sciences have a common interest in studying the BEHAVIOR of organisms. PSYCHOLOGY is one science that investigates the _____ of organisms.

1

behavior; organisms

8. While psychology is primarily concerned with studying the _____ of _____, PSYCHOLOGISTS are also interested in the internal "workings," or FUNCTIONS, of organisms.

functions/works
psychology

9. While psychology focuses on how man behaves, PSYCHOLOGISTS are also interested in how the brain FUNCTIONS ("works"). An understanding of how the brain _____ is important to the science of _____.

psychology

10. Similarly, psychologists study the functions of other organs of the body. How the eye and the ear function is of interest to the science of _____.

psychologists

11. The scientists who study psychology are called _____.

organisms

12. The science known as physiology is also concerned with studying the behavior of the different species of _____ in the world.

physiology

13. While physiology is interested in behavior, it is primarily concerned with the internal functions of the body. How the brain functions would thus not only be of interest to psychology, but would be a major concern of the science of _____.

physiology

14. So we can see that the sciences of psychology and _____ have much in common.

organisms

15. For one thing, psychologists and PHYSIOLOGISTS are both concerned with studying the behavior of _____.

function

16. For another, psychologists and physiologists are both concerned with how the internal organs of the body _____.

physiologists

17. The scientists who study physiology are called _____.

psychologist   *18.* A study performed on the behavior of a species like *Paramecium caudatum* might be conducted by a physiologist or by a _____ .

physiologist
psychologist
(either order)

19. Likewise, a study of the functioning of the brain might be conducted by either a _____ or by a _____ .

physiologist
psychologist
(either order)

20. If a study is performed on the behavior of man, it might be conducted by a _____ or by a _____ .

psychology
physiology
(either order)

21. Other sciences are also interested in behavior. But the only sciences concerned with both behavior and internal functions are the sciences of _____ and _____ .

organisms   *22.* Many factors influence the behavior of _____ .

behavior   *23.* One of these factors is the ENERGY that strikes the organism. Energy that strikes the organism may influence the _____ of that organism.

energy   *24.* Numerous types of _____ strike or impinge on organisms.

energy   *25.* An organism's behavior is influenced by the nature of the _____ that IMPINGES ("ĭm pĭnj'ĭz") on it.

impinges   *26.* The nature of the energy that strikes or _____ on an organism is one factor that determines behavior.

behavior   *27.* When a certain "bit" of energy influences the _____ of organisms we call that energy a STIMULUS.

stimulus

28.   Energy that impinges upon an organism is called a _____ if that energy affects behavior.

stimulus

29.   Any energy that affects, produces, or modifies behavior is called a _____.

organism

stimulus

30.   If energy that impinges on an organism does not activate the _____ to behave in some way, then we could not call that energy a _____.

energy

31.   One example of energy that would not activate an organism is when that _____ is extremely slight in intensity.

stimulus

32.   In this case, the energy is too "weak" to activate the organism and hence it could not be called a _____.

stimuli

organism

33.   The plural for stimulus is STIMULI. If a number of separate bits of energy impinge on an organism, we say that a number of different _____ are impinging on that _____.

stimulus

34.   A light is a specific type of energy. If a light impinges on an organism and causes the organism to behave, we call that light a _____.

stimulus

35.   If an organism comes in contact with the type of energy that we call an "odor," then that odor is a _____, provided that it activates the organism.

impinges

36.   Another example of a stimulus is when an intense sound strikes, or _____ on, an organism.

stimuli

37.   At any specific time, many, many, different _____ are impinging on any given organism.

impinge

38. The sum total of all stimuli that could _____ on an organism is called that organism's ENVIRONMENT.

stimulus

39. A specific _____ is, then, part of an organism's environment.

environment

40. An organism is always surrounded by a large number of stimuli. The sum total of those stimuli constitute the organism's _____.

environment

41. A wide variety of stimuli from an organism's _____ are constantly impinging on the organism to produce different kinds of behavior.

environment

42. When a specific type of stimulus from an organism's _____ impinges on that organism, it causes a specific type of behavior.

stimulus

behavior

43. We can thus say that a given _____ which impinges on an organism, produces a specific kind of _____.

behavior

44. The specific type of _____ that results from a given stimulus is called a RESPONSE.

45. If a baby touches a hot stove, he will immediately withdraw his hand. Withdrawing the hand is an example of the kind of behavior that we call a

response

_____.

46. If an extremely bright light impinges on an organism's eye, the pupil of the eye will contract. The

stimulus

very bright light is an example of a _____ and the contraction of the pupil is an example of the

response

kind of behavior that we call a _____.

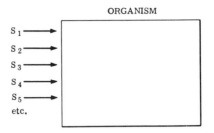

FIGURE 1

47. s_1 stands for one specific stimulus. s_2 stands for another stimulus, and so forth. Figure 1 shows that a

stimuli   large number of _____ are impinging on an organism.

stimuli   48. All of the _____ that could impinge on an organism are called that organism's

environment   _____.

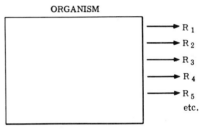

FIGURE 2

49. R_1 stands for a specific response, R_2 for another response, and so forth. Figure 2 shows that a large

responses   number of _____ are being made by an organism at any given time.

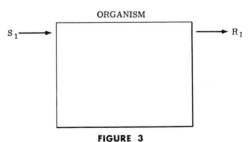

FIGURE 3

stimulus   50. Figure 3 shows that when a specific _____
response   (s_1) impinges on an organism a specific _____
(R_1) results.

FIGURE 4

51. In the top of Figure 4 we see an organism touching a hot stove. In the bottom of Figure 4 we see him withdrawing his hand from the hot stove. In this figure,

organism   A is the _____, the heat B is the

stimulus   _____, and C, the withdrawal of the

response   hand from the hot stove, is the _____.

52. In Figures 1, 2, and 3 we have represented the organism as a "box." The inside of the box represents

organism   the inside of the _____ and includes a variety of organs such as the heart, brain, and ears.

53. Just as the environment and behavior of an organism are very complex, the inside of the

organism   _____ is also very complex.

54. The sciences of psychology and physiology are both concerned with how the internal organs FUNCTION to produce the kind of behavior we call a

response   _____.

function   55. We shall now see how some of the internal organs _____ in order for responses to occur.

stimulus   56. When a _____ impinges on an organism, it activates, or excites a specific type of organ that we call a RECEPTOR.

stimulus   57. The eye is an example of a RECEPTOR. A light flashing in a person's eye is a _____ that can excite that receptor.

receptors   58. The more highly developed organisms possess many different types of _____ that can be excited by stimuli.

stimulus   59. A light is a specific type of _____
receptor   that EXCITES the _____ in the organism known as the eye.

stimuli   60. Sounds are _____ that EXCITE the
receptor   _____ known as the ear.

stimulus   61. An odor is the type of _____ that
excites   _____ the receptor known as the nose.

environment   62. Many types of stimuli from an organism's
receptors   _____ impinge on it to excite the various types of _____.

stimulus   63. Tiny nerves are connected to all receptors. When
receptor   a receptor is excited by a _____, the tiny nerve attached to the _____ is activated.

receptor   64. When a stimulus excites a _____, a NERVE IMPULSE is transmitted from the receptor and runs along the attached nerve.

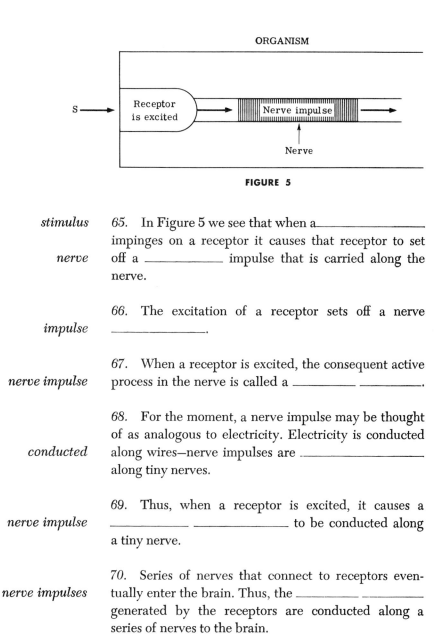

ORGANISM

FIGURE 5

stimulus   65. In Figure 5 we see that when a_____

impinges on a receptor it causes that receptor to set

nerve   off a _____ impulse that is carried along the

nerve.

66. The excitation of a receptor sets off a nerve

impulse   _____.

67. When a receptor is excited, the consequent active

nerve impulse   process in the nerve is called a _____ _____.

68. For the moment, a nerve impulse may be thought

of as analogous to electricity. Electricity is conducted

conducted   along wires—nerve impulses are _____

along tiny nerves.

69. Thus, when a receptor is excited, it causes a

nerve impulse   _____ _____ to be conducted along

a tiny nerve.

70. Series of nerves that connect to receptors even-

nerve impulses   tually enter the brain. Thus, the _____ _____

generated by the receptors are conducted along a

series of nerves to the brain.

71. At any given time, many of an organism's re-

stimuli   ceptors are being excited by many _____,

and, therefore, many different nerve impulses are

brain   being conducted simultaneously to the _____.

72. For example, when a sound excites the ear, a light might also be striking the organism's eye. In this case, we note that two _____ _____ are being simultaneously conducted to the brain.

nerve
impulses

73. Up to this point we have seen that an _____, be it a man, a dog, or a paramecium, is constantly receiving a large number of stimuli from his _____.

organism

environment

74. When these different stimuli _____ on the organism, its _____ are excited.

impinge
receptors

75. When the organism's receptors are_____, they generate _____ _____.

excited/activated
nerve impulses

76. The nerve impulses that are generated by receptors are then transmitted along tiny _____ to the _____.

nerves
brain

77. After nerve impulses arrive in the _____, they eventually leave it and are transmitted along series of nerves to effectors.

brain

78. There are two principal kinds of effectors: muscles are effectors, and glands are _____.

effectors

79. Because many _____ _____ are being conducted into the brain at any given time, many nerve impulses leave the brain at any given time and run to _____.

nerve impulses

effectors

80. Nerve impulses that leave the brain run to a number of different _____.

effectors

81. The body contains a very large number of muscles and glands. All of these _____ and _____ are effectors.

muscles
glands

effectors

82.   When one thinks about the very large number of muscles in the arms, legs, throat, etc., one begins to realize how very many _____, of the muscle type, the body contains.

glands

83.   We have said that muscles are effectors and that _____ are effectors.

sweat gland

84.   One kind of gland is the sweat gland. The _____ _____ is a specific type of effector.

effector

85.   The tear gland, which produces tears in the eyes, is another example of an _____.

receptors
nerve impulse
nerves; brain

86.   When a stimulus from an organism's environment impinges on one of its _____ a _____ _____ is generated that travels along tiny _____ to the _____.

effectors; muscles
glands

87.   The nerve impulse, then, eventually leaves the brain and typically arrives at one of two types of _____: _____ and _____.

nerve impulse

88.   When a _____ _____ arrives at an effector, that effector is ACTIVATED.

activated

89.   Although there are a number of different kinds of muscles and glands, any of these effectors may be _____ if they are stimulated by a nerve impulse.

effector

90.   When a nerve impulse leaves the brain and activates an _____, we say that a RESPONSE occurs.

response

91.   The activation of an effector results in a _____.

muscles
92. Responses occur in different ways for glands and _____ .

nerve impulse
93. A muscle CONTRACTS when it is activated by a _____ _____ .

response
94. When a muscle contracts, we say that a _____ occurs.

response
95. A nerve impulse that arrives at a muscle produces a _____ by causing the muscle to contract.

contracts
96. Another way of saying this is that the nerve impulse that arrives at a muscle is an internal stimulus. The nerve impulse thus stimulates the muscle, and the muscle _____ .

contracts
97. When a nerve impulse stimulates a muscle, the muscle _____ and a response occurs.

contracting
98. When a man makes a response, such as opening a door, we know that the muscles in his arms are _____ .

response
99. When a muscle contracts, a _____ occurs.

nerve impulses
100. All muscles contract when stimulated by _____ _____ , but this is not the case with glands.

glands
101. Each gland secretes a product. For example, the tear _____ secrete the product that we call tears.

sweat
102. The product secreted when the sweat glands are activated is called _____ .

glands
103. Whereas muscles contract when stimulated, various products are secreted when _____ are stimulated.

response

104. Essentially, an organism can make a response in two ways. When his muscles contract, or when his glands secrete a product, we say that a _____ occurs.

conducted

105. We can thus see that when a stimulus excites a receptor that receptor sets off a nerve impulse which is _____ along nerves to the brain.

effector

106. Eventually the nerve impulse leaves the brain and stimulates an _____.

contracts
gland

107. When the effector stimulated is a muscle, it _____, but if the effector stimulated is a _____, a product is secreted.

response

108. When either a muscle contracts, or a gland secretes a product, a _____ occurs.

109. To integrate what we have said so far, let us study Figure 6.

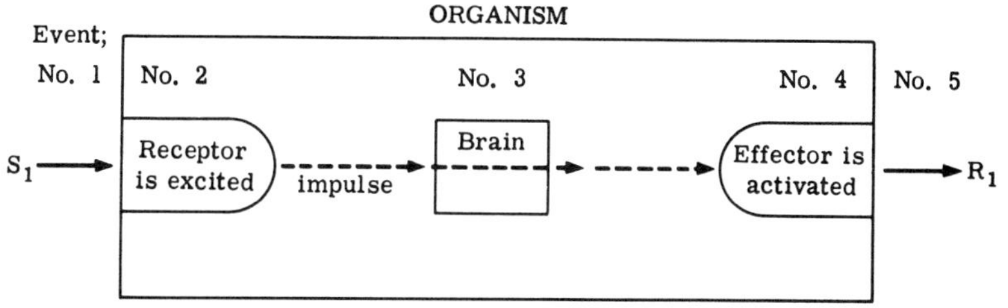

FIGURE 6

five

110. In Figure 6 we see _____ events labeled.

stimulus

111. Event No. 1 is a _____ impinging on an organism.

receptor

112. Event No. 2 indicates that the stimulus excites a _____ to set off a nerve impulse.

nerve impulse

effector

113. Event No. 3 shows the _____ _____ being conducted from the receptor through the brain and then finally to an _____.

activates

114. Event No. 4 shows that the nerve impulse _____ an effector.

response

115. Event No. 5 indicates the resulting _____.

environment
organism; receptor

116. To briefly summarize, let us note that when a stimulus from the _____ impinges on an _____, a _____ is excited.

nerve
impulse
brain

117. The excitation of a receptor sets off a _____ _____ that is conducted along a series of nerves into the _____.

conducted
effector

118. The nerve impulse eventually leaves the brain and is _____ along nerves to an _____.

contracts; gland

119. When the nerve impulse arrives at an effector, that effector is activated. If the effector is a muscle, it _____; but if the effector is a _____, it secretes its product.

response

120. The activation of an effector, be it a gland or a muscle, constitutes a _____.

impinges
response

121. Now we want to find out more specifically what happens inside an organism when a specific stimulus _____ on it and causes it to make a specific _____.

receptors

effectors

122. There are three general categories of organs, inside an organism, that we want to study. These are: (1) organs such as the eye and ear, called _____; (2) the collections of nerves that make up the nervous systems, including the brain, and (3) the different types of _____ (muscles and glands) that produce responses.

RECEPTORS

Section II: The Ear

impinge

123. We have said that an organism's environment consists of numerous types of energy that _____ on that organism.

stimulus

124. When energy from the environment excites a receptor, we call that energy a _____.

sense

125. The lay person typically believes that man possesses five "senses." To "explain" certain mystical phenomena, he then, sometimes, postulates the existence of a sixth _____ .

sense

126. Actually, however, man possesses more than six senses, with a unique type of receptor for each _____ .

environment

127. Each receptor is especially sensitive to a particular type of energy that comes from the organism's _____ .

ear

128. One type of energy that impinges on an organism is what we call SOUND WAVES. The receptor that is particularly sensitive to sound waves is the _____ .

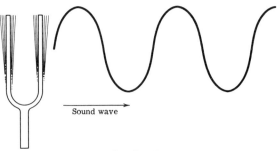

Sound wave

FIGURE 7

sound
waves

129. When an object, such as a tuning fork—which is part of a person's environment—is struck, it vibrates and typically sets off SOUND WAVES. Figure 7 shows a vibrating tuning fork that is sending _____ _____ through the air.

sound
waves

130. Usually there are many vibrating objects (auto horns, school bells, etc.) in a person's environment. These vibrating objects send numerous _____ _____ through the air.

sound waves

131. The _____ _____ from the many vibrating objects, then, typically impinge on a person's ear.

nerve
impulse

132. When a sound wave enters a person's ear, that receptor is normally excited, whereupon a _____ _____ in the attached nerve is started.

impinge

133. The ear, however, is not excited by all of the sound waves that _____ on it.

sound waves

receptor

134. There are two reasons for this. One reason is that not all of the _____ _____ are "strong" or "loud" (intense) enough to excite the _____ called the ear.

sound wave

excited/activated

135. That is, a _____ _____ that impinges on the ear must be of sufficient intensity (sufficiently "strong") before the ear can be _____.

sound wave   136.   If a _____ _____ is of extremely small intensity, then it may be too weak to excite the ear (it can't be "heard").

excited/activated   137.   The intensity of a sound wave determines whether or not the receptor will be _____.

intensity   138.   If the sound wave is very weak, then we say that it is of small _____.

intensity   139.   But if the sound wave is quite strong, then we say that its _____ is great.

sound
wave   140.   The minimum (least) intensity of a _____ _____ necessary to excite the ear is called the ABSOLUTE THRESHOLD of the ear.

threshold   141.   The concept of the ABSOLUTE THRESHOLD is very important. It applies to all of the receptors. In the case of the ear, if the sound stimulus is of sufficiently weak intensity, that stimulus is said to be below the absolute _____.

absolute   142.   If a sound wave is of rather great intensity (it can be "heard"), then it is above the _____ threshold.

absolute
threshold   143.   The minimum intensity of a sound wave necessary to excite the ear is the _____ _____ of the ear.

environment   144.   We previously saw that a stimulus consists of energy from an organism's _____.

energy   145.   The amount of stimulus ENERGY determines the intensity of the stimulus. Hence, the intensity of a sound wave is determined by the amount of _____ that it carries.

excite/activate   146.   The minimum stimulus energy, necessary to _____ a receptor, is called the absolute threshold.

absolute threshold

147.   The concept of the absolute threshold applies to all receptors. The minimum intensity of a light stimulus necessary to excite the eye is called the _____ _____ of the eye.

absolute
threshold

148.   The minimum stimulus energy of an odor, necessary to excite the nose, is the _____ _____ of that receptor.

excite/activate

149.   If a sound wave is extremely weak, it is below the absolute threshold of the ear and, thus, will not _____ the ear.

not

150.   Another reason that a sound wave might _____ excite the ear is that the ear is not capable of responding to all sound waves.

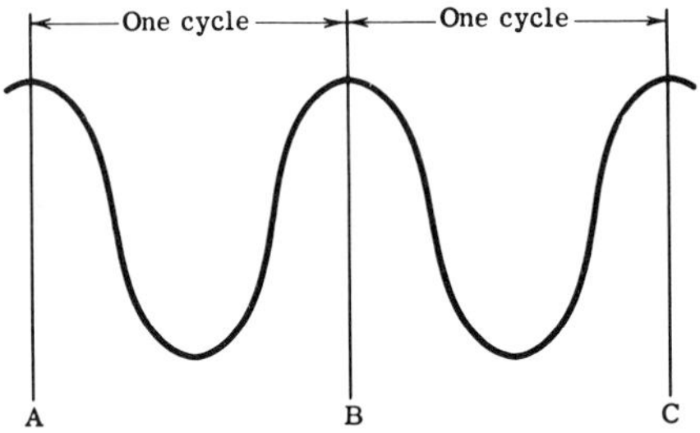

FIGURE 8

cycle

151.   To understand this, let us note that, in Figure 8, a sound wave is divided into CYCLES. The part of the sound wave between lines A and B indicates one _____.

cycles
sound wave

152.   One can count the number of _____ of a _____ _____ that occur during any given period of time.

cycles

153.   The FREQUENCY of a sound wave is the number of cycles that occur in one second. If one counts 1500 cycles occurring in one second, then one can say that the frequency of the sound wave is 1500 _____ PER SECOND.

154. If 20 cycles occur in one second, then the frequency of the sound wave is 20 cycles _____ _____.

per second

155. If 20,000 cycles occur in one second, then the FREQUENCY of the sound wave is 20,000 _____ _____ _____.

cycles per second

156. The human ear is generally capable of responding to any sound wave with a _____ between 20 cycles per second and about 20,000 _____ _____ _____.

frequency

cycles per second

157. Is the human ear capable of responding to a sound wave that has a frequency of 3 cycles per second? _____

No

158. Nor is the human ear capable of responding to a sound wave that has a _____ of 40,000 cycles per second.

frequency

159. We can thus see that the range of frequencies of sound (auditory) stimuli to which the ear can respond is restricted. That is, the ear cannot respond to an unlimited range of _____ of sound waves.

frequencies

160. The range of frequencies to which the ear is capable of responding is different for the different species. The ear of the dog, for instance, is capable of being excited by auditory (sound) stimuli of greater _____ than is the ear of man.

frequency

161. The dog whistle is based on this fact. The dog whistle emits sound waves with frequencies greater than 20,000 _____ _____ _____.

cycles per second

162. Since the dog whistle emits sound waves with frequencies _____ than 20,000 cycles per second, man cannot "hear" it.

greater

163. But since the dog's ear does respond to fre-
20,000   quencies above _____ cycles per second, a dog
can be trained to approach us at the sound of a dog
whistle.

164. The human ear is not capable of responding to
auditory stimuli below 20 cycles per second or above
20,000   _____ cycles per second.

165. The human ear will normally respond to its particular type of environmental energy provided (1)
frequency   that the _____ of the sound wave falls
within the range of 20 to 20,000 cycles per second; and
(2) that the intensity of the sound wave is above the
threshold   absolute _____.

166. Consider a sound wave that is above the absolute threshold and that is within the range of man's
20   ear: that is, it has a frequency between _____
20,000   and _____ cycles per second.

FIGURE 9   External ear

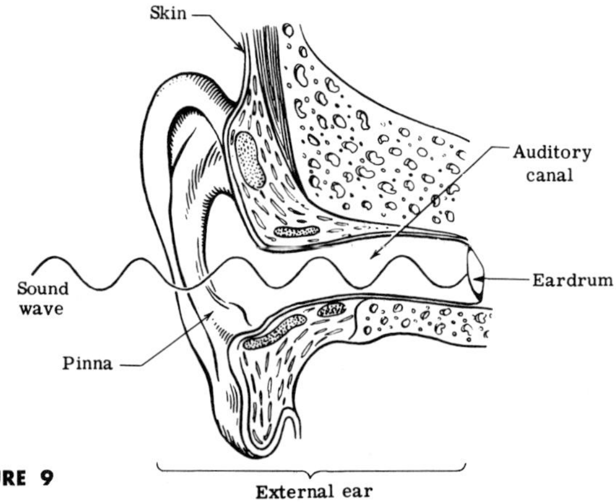

167. Study Figure 9, and note how such a sound
wave enters the ear. It first goes through the external
ear or PINNA. The function of the external ear, or
pinna   _____ is to collect sounds from the environment.

168. Sounds that are collected from the environment
pinna   by the _____ then travel through the auditory
canal.

auditory

169. As the sound waves travel through the _____ canal, they strike the eardrum.

pinna
auditory canal

170. Sound waves are collected by the _____, then travel through the _____ _____ until they come to the eardrum.

auditory canal

171. The eardrum is a very thin MEMBRANE (a thin, soft sheet of tissue) which is stretched across the end of the _____ _____.

eardrum

172. The varying pressure of the sound wave causes the membrane, called the _____, to vibrate (move back and forth).

membrane

173. When an auditory stimulus is conducted through the pinna, it is transmitted through the auditory canal and strikes the _____ called the eardrum.

vibrates

174. When an auditory stimulus strikes the eardrum, the eardrum _____ (moves back and forth).

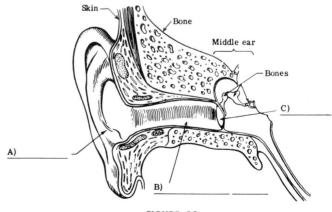

FIGURE 10

175. Identify the parts by filling in the blanks provided in Figure 10.

A. Pinna
B. Auditory canal
C. Eardrum

176. Figure 10 represents the middle ear. It shows that one of three small bones is attached to the

eardrum _____.

177. When the eardrum vibrates, the vibration is

bones carried through the three small _____ of the middle ear.

178. It can be seen in Figure 10 that the auditory

ear stimulus is conducted through the middle _____ by means of the vibrations carried along in the three small bones.

bones *179.* The three small _____ of the middle ear are called the OSSICLES (ŏs′ə kəlz).

180. The vibrations are conducted through the middle ear by means of three small bones called the

ossicles _____.

181. Sound waves enter the external ear, or

pinna; auditory _____, travel along the _____

canal _____, and then strike the eardrum.

182. When the sound waves strike the eardrum, the eardrum vibrates which, in turn, causes the ossicles

vibrate also to _____.

183. The vibration transmitted from the eardrum to the ossicles allows the sound to be conducted through

ear the middle _____.

middle *184.* The ossicles are in the _____ ear.

185. The ossicles are attached to the external ear

ear at the eardrum and to the part of the inner _____ called the COCHLEA (kŏk′lĭ ə).

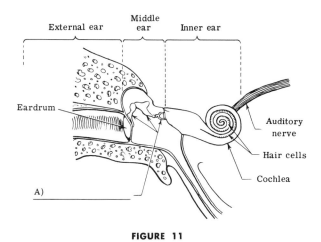

External ear   Middle ear   Inner ear

Eardrum

Auditory nerve

Hair cells

Cochlea

A) _____

FIGURE 11

A. Ossicles

186. Fill in the blank for Figure 11.

ossicles

187. In Figure 11 we see that the three small bones called the _____ are attached to the cochlea.

middle

ossicles

188. When the eardrum vibrates, the auditory stimulus is conducted through the _____ ear by means of the three bones called the _____ until the vibrations reach the cochlea.

cochlea

189. The word COCHLEA comes from the Greek word meaning "snail shell." This structure is called the _____ because it is spiraled like the shell of a snail.

cochlea

190. When the ossicles of the middle ear vibrate, the vibrations are transmitted to the _____.

inner

middle

191. The cochlea is located in the _____ ear and receives vibrations from the ossicles of the _____ ear.

cochlea

192. The inside of the structure that looks like a snail shell, called the _____, contains a fluid.

cochlea; inner   193. The _____ is a part of the _____ ear and contains fluid.

ossicles; vibrations   194. When the cochlea receives vibrations from the _____, those _____ cause changes in the pressure of the fluid contained in the cochlea.

fluid
cochlea   195. The cochlea contains _____. The _____ also contains tiny sensory cells called HAIR CELLS.

cochlea   196. When the ossicles transmit vibrations to the fluid inside the _____, variations in pressure of that fluid occur.

fluid   197. The variation of the pressure of the _____ inside the cochlea stimulates the tiny hair cells.

pressure

hair cells   198. The variation of the _____ of the fluid inside the cochlea stimulates the tiny sensory cells called _____ _____.

hair
cells   199. The change of pressure of the fluid inside the cochlea exerts vibratory pressure on the _____ _____.

auditory
canal; eardrum   200. When a sound wave is picked up by the pinna, it is transmitted along the _____ _____ until it strikes the _____.

middle   201. The vibrations are then transmitted from the external ear, through the _____ ear, by means of the ossicles.

inner   202. The cochlea, located in the _____ ear, then receives those vibrations.

fluid   203. Once the cochlea receives vibrations, changes in the pressure of the _____ inside it occur.

pressure
hair cells

204. These changes in the _____ of the fluid stimulate the tiny _____ _____ inside the cochlea.

205. Numerous tiny nerves are attached to the hair cells. These tiny _____ group together to form part of a major nerve called the auditory nerve.

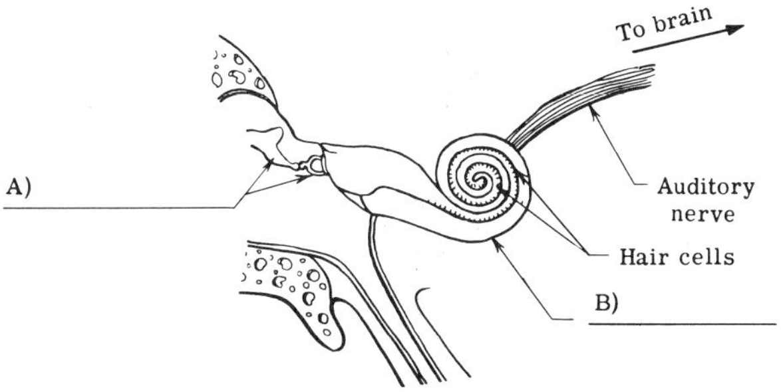

nerves

To brain

A) _____

Auditory nerve

Hair cells

B) _____

FIGURE 12

A. Ossicles
B. Cochlea

206. Identify the structures in Figure 12 by filling in the blanks.

nerve

207. In Figure 12 we see that the auditory _____ runs from the hair cells of the cochlea to the brain.

inner
brain

208. The auditory nerve is a major nerve that runs from the cochlea, located in the _____ ear, to the

auditory; brain

209. When the hair cells are stimulated, they set off nerve impulses that are transmitted along the _____ nerve to the _____.

auditory nerve

210. The stimulation of the hair cells sets off nerve impulses that are transmitted to the brain by means of the _____ _____.

211. Let us now summarize what we have learned by stating the events that occur in the receipt of an auditory stimulus.

212. Event No. 1: The vibration of a stimulus object produces a stimulus in the form of a sound _____. This sound wave is called a sound or _____ stimulus.

wave
auditory

213. Event No. 2: That sound wave is transmitted through the air and is collected by the external _____ or PINNA.

ear

214. Event No. 3: Once the _____ collects the sound wave, it transmits vibrations through the auditory canal.

pinna

215. Event No. 4: When the auditory stimulus is collected by the pinna and transmitted through the _____ _____, it strikes the eardrum.

auditory canal

216. Event No. 5: When the sound wave strikes the _____ it causes that membrane to vibrate. The sound wave can only cause the membrane to vibrate sufficiently to transmit the sound if two things happen: (1) if the frequency of the sound wave is between 20 and 20,000 _____ _____ _____; and (2) if the intensity of the sound wave is above the _____ _____ of the ear.

eardrum

cycles per
second
absolute threshold

217. If the frequency of the sound wave is not between 20 and 20,000 cycles per second, or if its intensity is below the absolute threshold, then the sound wave cannot be called an _____ stimulus for the human ear.

auditory

middle
ossicles

218. Event No. 6: When the eardrum vibrates, it causes the three bones of the _____ ear called the _____ to vibrate.

vibrations

219. Event No. 7: The auditory stimulus is thus transmitted through the middle ear as a series of _____ of the ossicles.

inner

cochlea

220. Event No. 8: These ossicles are attached to the part of the _____ ear known as the cochlea. The vibrations of the ossicles are thus transmitted to the _____.

fluid

221. Event No. 9: The vibrations received by the cochlea produce changes in the pressure of the _____ inside it.

cochlea

222. Event No. 10: The change of pressure in the fluid of the _____ is transmitted to the hair cells.

hair cells

223. Event No. 11: When the pressure of the fluid inside the cochlea changes, it stimulates the tiny sense cells called the _____ _____.

nerves

224. Event No. 12: When the hair cells are stimulated, they set off nerve impulses that are conducted along the tiny _____ that are attached to them.

auditory nerve

225. Event No. 13: When the hair cells are stimulated, the nerve impulses, thereby produced, are conducted along the group of tiny nerves that form the major nerve called the _____ _____.

brain

226. Event No. 14: The auditory nerve then conducts the nerve impulses to the _____.

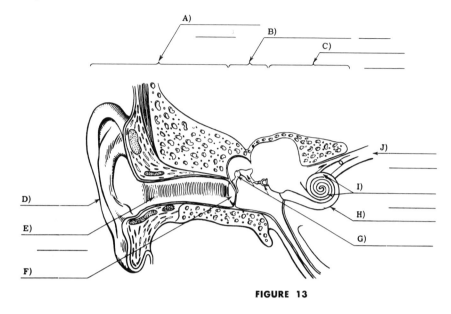

FIGURE 13

A. *External Ear*

B. *Middle Ear*

C. *Inner Ear*

D. *Pinna*

E. *Auditory Canal*

F. *Eardrum*

G. *Ossicles*

H. *Cochlea*

I. *Hair Cells*

J. *Auditory Nerve*

227. In Figure 13, write in the parts of the ear, in the blanks provided.

228. Without looking at the preceding discussion, draw a diagram of the parts of the external, the middle, and the inner ear, concluding with the auditory nerve that runs to the brain. State each step that occurs, from the point at which a vibrating object sends off a sound wave, to the point where a nerve impulse is transmitted to the brain. Be sure to label each part of the ear. Then check your diagram and steps for accuracy against the preceding discussion. (Standard size notebook paper may be used for all drawings that appear in this book.)

RECEPTORS

Section III: The Eye

auditory

brain

229. We have just seen how the type of energy that we call an _____ stimulus leaves a vibrating stimulus object, impinges on the ear, and sets off a nerve impulse that runs to the _____.

230. In like manner, we shall now trace the process by which the type of environmental energy, that we call a visual stimulus, leaves a stimulus object and sets off a nerve impulse that runs from the receptor,

eye

called the _____, to the brain.

231. Some stimulus objects emit what we call RADIANT (rā′dĭ ənt) ENERGY. A light bulb is an example of a

stimulus

_____ object that emits radiant energy.

232. Consider the various stimulus objects, in a person's environment, that emit RADIANT ENERGY. A stimulus object, such as a light bulb, itself produces

energy

the radiant _____ that it emits.

233. Other stimulus objects, however, do not produce

radiant

radiant energy, but rather they reflect _____ energy coming from other sources.

234. For example, a light bulb in a room produces radiant energy that strikes the wall. That radiant energy is then reflected from the wall and is trans-

receptor

mitted to the organism's visual _____ that we call the eye.

235.   Another example of a stimulus object that itself
radiant energy   emits _____ _____, is a lighted
match.

236.   A desk is an example of a stimulus object that
radiant energy   reflects, rather than emits, _____ _____.

237.   One way of characterizing radiant energy is in
terms of waves. In the case of auditory stimuli, we
talked about sound WAVES; in the case of visual stimuli,
waves   we shall talk about light _____.

238.   A stimulus object, such as a light bulb, gives off
radiant energy that can be described in terms of
waves   light _____.

239.   Light waves are produced by stimulus objects
radiant   that give off _____ energy.

radiant   240.   When a stimulus object gives off _____
energy   _____, light waves are produced.

241.   The radiant energy given off by visual stimuli
light   produces _____ waves of a much greater frequency than is the case for sound waves.

242.   Because the frequency of light waves is greater
light   than the frequency of sound waves, _____
waves   _____ travel much faster than do sound waves.

243.   To be more precise, sound waves travel about
light   1,100 feet per second, whereas _____
waves   _____ travel about 186,000 miles per
second.

244.   We previously saw that the human ear cannot
be excited by all frequencies of sound waves. In like
manner, all frequencies of radiant energy cannot be
eye   "picked up" by the human _____.

frequencies

245. While the eye can be excited by certain frequencies of radiant energy, it cannot be excited by other _____.

eye

246. Infrared rays are an example of a frequency that is too slow to activate the human _____.

frequencies
excite/activate

247. Radar and radio waves are other examples of _____ of radiant energy that are too slow to _____ the human eye.

radiant
excite/activate

248. Ultraviolet rays, x-rays, and gamma rays are frequencies of _____ energy that are too fast to _____ the human eye.

excite

249. The frequencies that can _____ the eye are called the VISIBLE SPECTRUM.

energy

250. The visual stimuli to which we respond are the frequencies of radiant _____ which constitute the visible spectrum.

FREQUENCY OF WAVES

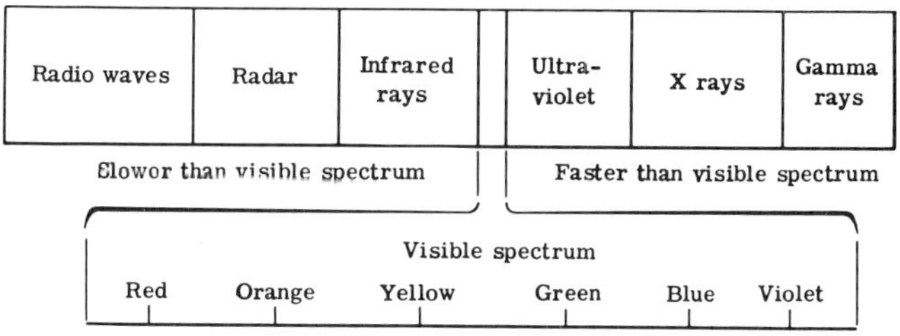

Radio waves	Radar	Infrared rays	Ultra-violet	X rays	Gamma rays

Slower than visible spectrum | Faster than visible spectrum

Visible spectrum

| Red | Orange | Yellow | Green | Blue | Violet |

FIGURE 14

spectrum

251. In Figure 14, we can see a representation of various frequencies. Note that gamma rays, x-rays, and ultraviolet rays have a frequency greater than that of the visible _____.

visible spectrum

252. On the other hand, infrared rays, radar waves, and radio waves are lower in frequency than the _____ _____.

253. We cannot see infrared rays because their frequency is less than that of the _____ _____.

visible
spectrum

254. The human eye can only be excited by _____ of radiant energy that fall within the _____ _____.

frequencies
visible spectrum

255. Frequencies of radiant energy that fall above or below the visible spectrum cannot _____ the human eye.

excite/activate

256. A light wave is radiant energy that has a frequency in the region of the _____ _____.

visible
spectrum

257. The visible spectrum can be divided into frequencies for the different colors. For example, one particular frequency within the _____ _____ is that for red light.

visible
spectrum

258. A frequency of light waves greater than that for red is the frequency for blue light. The _____ for blue and red light both fall within the _____ _____.

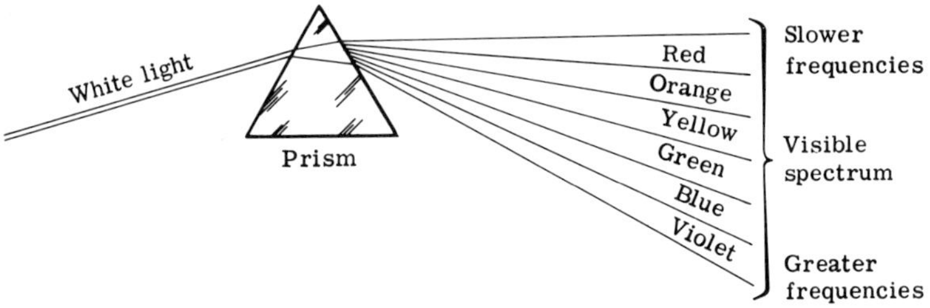

frequencies
visible spectrum

FIGURE 15

259. In Figure 15, we see the colors that constitute the visible spectrum. Note that the frequency of blue light is _____ than the frequency of red light.

greater/faster/
higher

260. A light _____ may be a VISUAL STIMULUS.

wave

radiant
light waves

261.   Remember that visual stimulus objects give off
_____ energy which travels through the air
in the form of _____ _____.

radiant energy

262.   Light bulbs and the sun are examples of stimulus
objects that emit _____ _____
in the form of light waves.

stimulus

263.   If a light wave impinges on a person's eye and
excites the eye, we call that light wave a visual
_____.

visible
spectrum

264.   Visual stimuli are light waves that have frequencies that fall within the _____
_____.

radiant energy

265.   A visual stimulus can come from any object that
we can see. While some objects themselves emit
_____ _____ in the form of light
waves, other objects REFLECT it.

reflect

266.   A book or a picture are examples of objects
that do not emit radiant energy, but rather they
_____ it from other sources.

reflected

267.   The eye can thus be excited by light waves that
are either emitted or _____ from stim-
ulus objects.

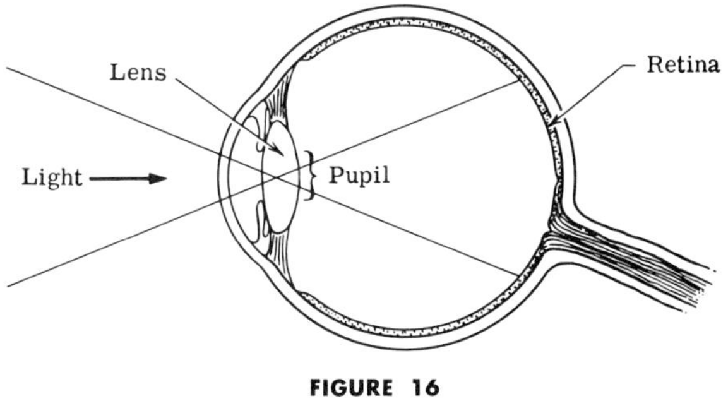

FIGURE 16

eye

268.   In Figure 16, we see a representation of light
entering the human _____.

retina (rĕt'ə nə)

269. As shown in Figure 16, the light first passes through the PUPIL and LENS. The light finally falls on the _____ of the eye.

closes

270. The pupil is regulated by a group of muscles. As these muscles contract and relax, the PUPIL opens and _____.

pupil

271. The pupil is the black center that we see when we look in a person's eye. The _____ is simply an opening that changes in size to admit smaller and larger amounts of light.

light
pupil

272. As varying amounts of _____ enter the eye, the opening that we call the _____ changes in size.

pupil

273. The opening in the eye, through which light travels, is called the _____.

stimulus

274. The lens of the eye is similar in function to the lens of a camera. The function of the lens of the eye is to focus the image of a _____ object onto the RETINA.

lens
retina

275. As the muscles that regulate the lens contract and relax, the LENS changes its shape. By changing its shape, the _____ assures that a sharp image of the stimulus object falls on the _____.

retina

276. Hence, when we look at a stimulus object, a picture or image of it falls on the _____ of the eye.

retina

277. Now let us look at the retina of the eye in a little more detail. The _____ covers most of the inside of the eye.

retina

278. The image of a stimulus object passes through the lens and falls on the inside of the eye that we call the _____.

279. As the intensity of light that comes from an

environment   organism's _____ changes, the

muscles of a person's eye change.

280. Recall that as the muscles of a person's eye

contract and relax, the shape of the lens changes.

lens   These modifications in the shape of the _____

produce a sharp image of the stimulus object on the

retina   _____.

281. When the lens changes its shape, it FOCUSES the

stimulus object. The reason that a sharp image falls

lens   on the retina of the eye is because the _____

focuses it.

focus   282. The function of the lens is to _____ a

stimulus object so that a sharp image of it will fall

on the retina.

focus   283. If the lens did not _____ the stimulus

object, the image on the retina would be fuzzy rather

than sharp and clear.

284. Some stimulus objects, in a person's environ-

radiant energy   ment, themselves emit _____ _____

in the form of light waves.

285. Other stimulus objects, however, do not emit

reflect   radiant energy, but rather they _____ it

from other sources.

286. In either case these light waves are visual stim-

excite   uli if they impinge on an organism and _____

that organism's eye.

287. All visual stimuli have frequencies that fall

visible spectrum   within the _____ _____.

288. The color of the stimulus object that the per-

frequency   son sees depends on the _____ of the

light waves that come from it.

frequency

289.   For example, if the frequency is quite slow, the person may see red. Light waves from blue objects, however, have a greater or higher _____ than do those from red objects.

pupil

290.   When a light wave first enters a person's eye, it goes through the opening (that looks like a black center) called the _____, and then through the lens.

focus

retina

291.   The function of the lens is to _____ the stimulus object so that a sharp image will fall on the _____.

retina

292.   It is possible to actually look inside a person's eye and see the image of a stimulus object on the person's _____.

retina

293.   The retina of the eye contains two kinds of tiny cells called RODS and CONES. There are a very large number of rods and cones in the _____ of the eye.

retina

294.   Just to give you a rough idea, it has been estimated that there are approximately 120,000,000 rods and 6,500,000 cones in the _____ of the human eye.

rods

cones

295.   Rods and cones are cells contained in the retina. These cells are called _____ and _____ because of their shape.

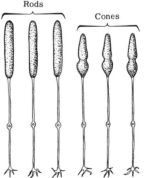

Rods   Cones

FIGURE 17

cones

296.   As you can see in Figure 17, rods are cylindrical in shape whereas _____ are rather tapered.

297. Rods and cones are typically both excited when
retina   an image of a stimulus object falls on the _____ .

298. Rods, however, are used in "black-white vision,"
cones   whereas _____ are used in "color vision."

299. You can always remember this difference if you
note that the first two letters of "cones" and "color" are
the same. Hence, rods are used in black-white vision,
cones; color   whereas _____ are used in _____
vision.

300. For example, if you are looking at a colored
cones   object, the _____ are the cells of the retina that
are excited.

301. Because they are used in black-white vision,
rods   _____ are the cells that function at night-time.

302. Thus, if a person looks at a stimulus object at
rods; cones   night, his _____ are excited, but his _____
are not excited.

303. The old saying "at night all cats are gray"
illustrates this point. That is, even a yellow cat would
look gray at night because this stimulus object would
cones   not excite the _____ of the retina.

cones   *304.* Connected to the rods and _____ are
two other types of cells in the retina, of interest to us.
These are called bipolar cells and ganglion cells.

rods   *305.* The cones and _____ are at the bottom or
retina   back of the _____ .

306. Just above (in front of) the layer of the retina
cones   that contains rods and _____ , one finds the
BIPOLAR CELLS.

rods   *307.* The bipolar cells are connected to the _____
cones   and _____ .

cell

308. The type of cell that is connected to the rods and cones is called the bipolar _____.

bipolar

309. Rods and cones are in the bottom layer of the retina. Just above them are _____ cells.

bipolar cell

310. The name of the cell that is connected to the rods and cones is the _____ _____.

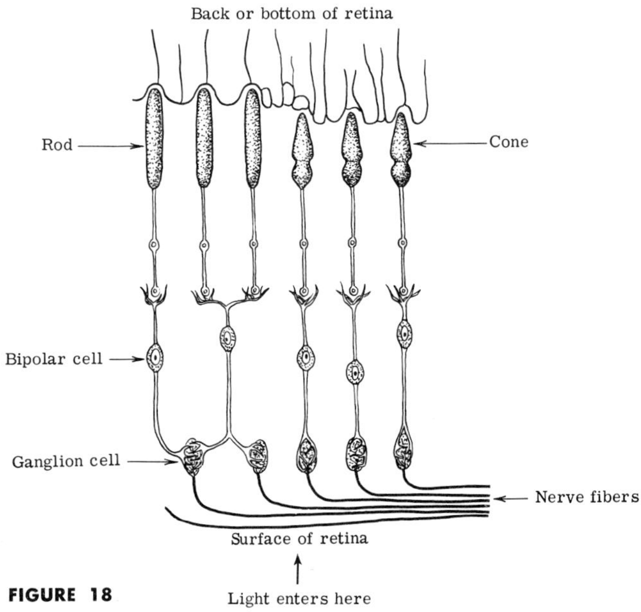

Back or bottom of retina

Rod ——

——Cone

Bipolar cell ——►

Ganglion cell ——►

◄— Nerve fibers

Surface of retina

FIGURE 18   Light enters here

cell

311. As can be seen in Figure 18, the bipolar cell is connected to another type of cell called the GANGLION CELL. For our present purposes, the bipolar _____ may be thought of as simply a link in a chain.

ganglion

312. The bipolar cell is connected to the _____ cell.

bipolar cells

313. Rods and cones are connected to _____ _____ which, in turn, are connected to ganglion cells.

ganglion cell

314. The name of the cell that is connected to the bipolar cell is the _____ _____.

315. As can be seen in Figure 18, the end of the

ganglion ———————————— cell is a tiny nerve fiber which can conduct a nerve impulse.

316. We can thus see that the retina contains three

rods layers of cells. At the bottom one finds ————————

cones and ————————.

bipolar 317. The next layer contains ————————————————

cells ———————————— that connect to the rods and cones.

318. And in the surface or top layer, connected to

ganglion the bipolar cells, one finds ————————————————

cells ————————.

319. The end of each ganglion cell is a tiny

nerve ———————————— fiber that can conduct a nerve impulse.

320. Consider that light waves from an object pass through the pupil and lens, thus projecting an image

retina of the object on the surface of the ————————.

321. The radiant energy of the light waves that form the image is transmitted to the bottom or back of the

cones retina where it stimulates rods and ————————.

322. When the radiant energy from a stimulus ob-

retina ject reaches the back of the ————————, a CHEMICAL reaction occurs.

323. Light falling on the retina sets off a chemical

rods reaction that stimulates ———————— and cones.

324. When light waves from a stimulus object fall on the retina to form an image, the radiant energy of

chemical those light waves produces a ————————————————

reaction.

reaction 325. That chemical ———————————————— then ex-

rods; cones cites the ———————— and ————————.

excited/activated   326.   When the rods and cones are _____, a nerve impulse is set off.

impulse   327.   This nerve _____ is then transmitted
cells   to the bipolar _____.

bipolar; nerve   328.   The _____ cells receive _____
impulses   _____ that are set off by the rods and cones.

329.   When a nerve impulse is set off by the rods and
cones, that nerve impulse is received by the
bipolar cells   _____ _____.

bipolar   330.   When a nerve impulse is generated by the rods
and cones, it is received by the _____ cells
and is then transmitted to the ganglion cells.

331.   The bipolar cells transmit nerve impulses to the
ganglion   _____ cells.

332.   You will recall that the ends of the ganglion
cells are tiny nerve fibers. These nerve fibers of the
ganglion   _____ cells make up the OPTIC NERVE.

333.   The nerve fibers that are the end of the ganglion
nerve   cells form a major nerve called the optic _____.

optic   334.   The major nerve called the _____
nerve runs from the eye to the brain.

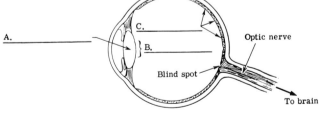

A.

C.

B.

Optic nerve

Blind spot

To brain

FIGURE 19

A. *Lens*   335.   Write in the parts of the eye in the blanks pro-
B. *Pupil*   vided.
C. *Retina*

optic
brain
   336. Figure 19 shows the _____ nerve leaving the eye and running to the _____ .

nerve impulse
   337. When a ganglion cell receives a nerve impulse, that _____ _____ is transmitted along the nerve fibers of the ganglion cell that compose the optic nerve.

optic nerve
   338. In this way the nerve impulse is transmitted along the _____ _____ to the brain.

ganglion
   339. The optic nerve is made up of nerve fibers of the _____ cells.

optic
nerve
   340. The nerve that transmits nerve impulses from the eye to the brain is called the _____ _____ .

spot

optic
   341. Note the blind spot in Figure 19. The blind _____ is a place in the retina where the tiny nerve fibers of the ganglion cells congregate to form the _____ nerve.

blind

rods
   342. Because the _____ spot consists exclusively of nerve fibers, it does not contain cones and _____ .

impulse
   343. Since there are no rods and cones in the blind spot of the retina, an image of a stimulus object falling at that place cannot set off a nerve _____ .

blind spot
   344. Hence, we cannot see the part of a stimulus object that falls on the _____ _____ .

blind spot
   345. Kings used to use this fact for their enjoyment: they would close one eye and look at the court jester in such a way that the jester's head would fall on the _____ _____ .

346.   If the king liked the way the jester looked without a head, he would have the jester beheaded. With a little practice, you can note that a part of an object cannot be seen if you cause its image to fall on the

blind spot   _____ _____ of one of your eyes.

347.   We can thus see that the following events occur

stimulus   in the receipt of a visual _____.

348.   Event No. 1: A stimulus object either emits or

radiant   reflects _____ energy.

349.   Event No. 2: The radiant energy is then trans-

light   mitted to the eye in the form of _____ waves.

350.   Event No. 3: The light waves first pass through

pupil   the _____ and lens of the eye.

351.   Event No. 4: As the light rays pass through it,

lens   they are focused by the _____ of the eye.

352.   Event No. 5: The lens causes a sharp image of

retina   the stimulus object to fall on the _____ of the eye.

353.   Event No. 6: When the light rays form an

retina   image on the _____ of the eye, the tiny cells

rods; cones   called the _____ and _____ are stimulated.

354.   Event No. 7: When the rods and cones are

nerve impulses   stimulated, they set off _____ _____.

355.   Event No. 8: The nerve impulses set off by the

rods; cones   _____ and _____ are transmitted to the bipolar cells.

356.   Event No. 9: The nerve impulse is then con-

bipolar cells   ducted along the _____ _____ and is thus transmitted to the ganglion cells.

357. Event No. 10: When the nerve impulse is received by the _____ cells, that nerve impulse is conducted along the _____ nerve to the _____.

ganglion
optic
brain

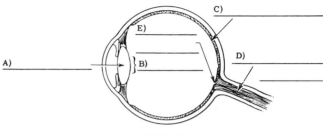

FIGURE 20

358. Label each part of the eye in the blanks provided in Figure 20.

A. *Lens*
B. *Pupil*
C. *Retina*
D. *Optic nerve*
E. *Blind spot*

359. Without looking at the preceding discussion, draw a diagram of light entering the eye, and specify each event that occurs between the point at which the light enters the eye and the point at which the resulting nerve impulse leaves the eye to be conducted to the brain. After you have done this, go back and check yourself against the material you have just read.

RECEPTORS

Section IV: Olfaction

smell

360. We have briefly seen how the eye and ear work. Let us now consider how the receptor cells in the nose respond to a SMELL. The nose contains receptor cells that are particularly sensitive to a _____.

smell

361. OLFACTION is the technical term for the sense of _____.

olfaction

362. When we want to talk about the sense of smell, we will usually use the term _____.

stimuli

363. When talking about smell, we will refer to OLFACTORY stimuli instead of smell _____.

olfactory

364. Thus, we say that the nose is particularly sensitive to _____ stimuli.

olfactory

365. The type of stimulus that excites the nose is the _____ stimulus.

Olfactory

366. _____ stimuli are odors.

odors

367. A number of stimulus objects in our environment give off ODORS. These _____ are potential olfactory stimuli.

odors

368. Odors are in a gaseous state. More particularly these _____ are a mixture of air and the MOLECULES (mŏl′ə kūl) that come from the stimulus objects.

molecule

369. For our present purposes, we may think of MOLECULES as tiny particles. A _____ is a tiny particle.

molecules

370. Stimulus objects consist of MOLECULES. Some of these _____ leave the stimulus objects to enter the air.

molecules

371. When a stimulus object, such as a cup of coffee, emits molecules, these _____ mix with the air to create an ODOR.

odor

372. When molecules from an object mix with air, an _____ is created.

environment

odor

373. There are numerous stimulus objects in our _____ that give off molecules. When these molecules mix with air, an _____ is produced.

odor

374. When molecules leave a can of paint, they mix with air to produce an _____.

molecules

375. The odor of paint, then, is a kind of gas that contains _____ from the paint.

stimulus

odor

376. Consider an odor that leaves a _____ object and comes in contact with a person's nose. How does the _____ stimulate the person's nose?

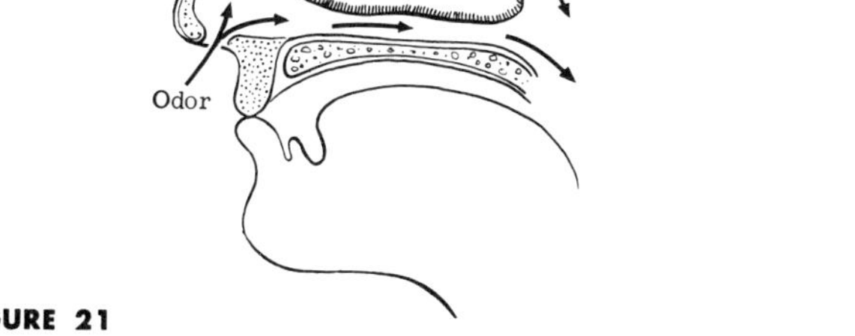

FIGURE 21

odor

377. In Figure 21, we see a diagram of a human nose. The arrows indicate the path of an _____ as it enters the nose.

cavity

378. Figure 21 indicates that the odors have entered the nasal cavity. At the top of the nasal _____ you can see the olfactory receptors.

nasal

379. The olfactory receptors are at the top of the _____ cavity.

nasal cavity

380. There are numerous olfactory receptors at the top of the _____ _____.

receptors

381. When we breathe in odors, these odors enter the nasal cavity and come in contact with olfactory _____.

olfactory

382. We recall that odors contain molecules. When an odor enters the nasal cavity, molecules come in contact with the _____ receptors.

nasal cavity

383. When the molecules that are contained in odors enter the _____ _____, they come in contact with olfactory receptors.

olfactory

384. The molecules in an odor may excite the _____ receptors.

excite/activate

385. If an odor does _____ the olfactory receptors, a nerve impulse is generated.

olfactory
receptors

386. Just as in the case of the receptors in the eye and ear, however, the _____ _____ will not be excited by all odors.

excited

387. That is, the intensity of the odor that comes in contact with olfactory receptors must be above the absolute threshold in order for them to be _____.

absolute

388. If the intensity of an odor is above the _____ threshold of the olfactory receptors, then those receptors will set off nerve impulses.

absolute
threshold

389. The olfactory receptors will not respond to an odor if its intensity is below the _____ _____ _____.

odor

390. The intensity of an _____ is dependent upon the number of molecules per unit of air.

molecules

391. An odor is rather intense if a certain amount of air contains a lot of _____.

intense/strong

392. But if the air contains relatively few molecules, the odor is not very _____.

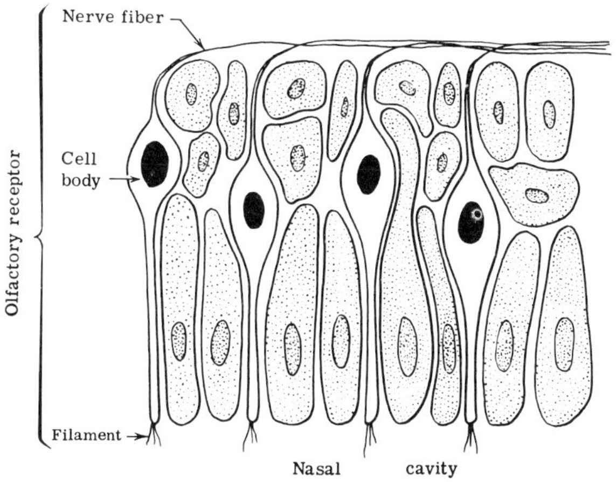

FIGURE 22

olfactory
receptors

393. In Figure 22, we see that _____ _____ are tiny cells.

394. The first part of the olfactory receptor is a fine FILAMENT, or "hair." This filament is the part that *cavity* projects into the nasal _____.

cell

395. Note that the middle part of the olfactory receptor is the CELL BODY. A _____ body is the part of any cell that nourishes it and "keeps it alive."

nerve

396. The last part of the olfactory receptor is a tiny NERVE FIBER. The _____ fiber is the part that conducts a nerve impulse toward the brain.

olfactory
receptor

397. As you can see, in Figures 21 and 22, the filament (hair) is the part of the _____ _____ that is exposed in the nasal cavity.

filament/hair

398. Thus, the part of the olfactory receptor that comes in contact with the molecules contained in an odor is the _____.

nasal cavity

399. When the molecules contained in an odor enter the _____ _____, they strike the filaments of the olfactory receptors.

filaments

400. When these molecules strike the _____ of the olfactory receptors, nerve impulses are set off.

nerve impulses

401. The activation of the filaments by molecules sets off _____ _____.

olfactory receptor

402. In this event, the nerve impulse is conducted through the cell body and along the nerve fiber part of the _____ _____.

nerve impulses

403. When molecules activate the filaments of olfactory receptors, _____ _____ are conducted through the olfactory receptors.

filament

cell body
nerve
fiber

404. In short, the molecules of an odor activate the part of the olfactory receptor called the _____, which sets off a nerve impulse that runs through the middle part called the _____ _____, and finally along the last part called the _____ _____.

nasal cavity

405. We know that the filament end of the olfactory receptor projects into the _____ _____.

fiber

top

406. Because the nerve FIBER is the TOP part of the olfactory receptor, we know that the nerve _____ points in the direction toward the _____ of the head.

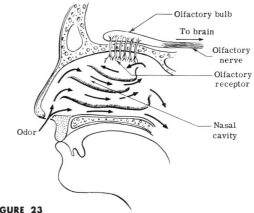

Olfactory bulb

To brain

Olfactory nerve

Olfactory receptor

Nasal cavity

Odor

FIGURE 23

407. In Figure 23, we can see that the olfactory receptors connect to the OLFACTORY BULB. The nerve fiber end is the part of the olfactory receptor that

olfactory connects to the _____ bulb.

olfactory *408.* The _____ bulb is made up of a number of tiny nerves.

409. The nerve fibers at the end of the olfactory receptors connect to the tiny nerves in the olfactory

bulb _____.

410. We can thus see that when the olfactory receptor is excited, a nerve impulse is conducted to the

olfactory bulb tiny nerves in the _____ _____.

411. Nerve impulses enter the olfactory bulb from

nerve fibers the _____ _____ of the olfactory receptors.

412. Since the olfactory bulb is made up of a number of tiny nerves, nerve impulses may be conducted

filament through it. When molecules strike the _____ of the olfactory receptor, a nerve impulse is generated that runs through the cell body and along the

nerve fiber _____ _____ to the tiny nerves of the olfactory bulb.

olfactory bulb

413. The nerve impulse then runs through the _____ _____.

(read on)

414. Where does the nerve impulse go when it leaves the olfactory bulb? Study Figure 23 and write your answer: _____.

brain

415. As shown in Figure 23, the nerves in the olfactory bulb connect to a major nerve that runs to the _____.

olfactory

416. The nerve that connects the olfactory bulb to the brain is called the _____ nerve.

olfactory bulb

417. So we can see that a nerve impulse that leaves the _____ _____ is transmitted to the olfactory nerve.

olfactory nerve

418. The nerve that runs from the olfactory bulb to the brain is called the _____ _____.

olfactory nerve

419. Thus, nerve impulses actually enter the brain by means of the _____ _____.

olfactory
nerve

420. When a nerve impulse is transmitted from the olfactory receptors to the olfactory bulb, it is further transmitted to the brain by means of the _____ _____.

421. Let us now summarize the events that occur in normal olfaction:

molecules

422. Event No. 1: A stimulus object in a person's environment gives off odors that contain _____.

odor

423. Event No. 2: When the molecules of the _____ enter a person's nose, they pass into the nasal cavity.

nasal cavity

424. Event No. 3: Once the molecules of the odor reach the roof of the _____ _____, they come in contact with the filaments of the olfactory receptors.

filament

425. Event No. 4: When the molecules contained in an odor strike the _____ of an olfactory receptor, a nerve impulse is set off.

nerve
impulse
nerve fiber

426. Event No. 5: That _____ _____ is then conducted through the cell body and the _____ _____ of the olfactory receptor.

427. Event No. 6: When a nerve impulse leaves the olfactory receptors, it is next transmitted to the

olfactory bulb

_____ _____.

428. Event No. 7: The nerve impulse then leaves the olfactory bulb and is transmitted to the brain by means

olfactory nerve

of the _____ _____.

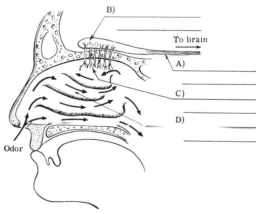

FIGURE 24

429. Label the parts of the nose in the blanks provided in Figure 24.

A. *Olfactory Nerve*
B. *Olfactory Bulb*
C. *Olfactory Receptors*
D. *Nasal Cavity*

430. Without looking at the preceding discussion, draw a diagram showing each step from the point at which an odor leaves a stimulus object until the nerve impulse is conducted to the brain.

RECEPTORS

Section V: Gustation

taste

431. The sense of taste may also be called the sense of gustation. GUSTATION is the technical term for _____.

gustation

432. Sometimes we will use the word taste, and sometimes the word _____.

gustatory

433. Hence, a taste stimulus may be referred to as a GUSTATORY stimulus. Rather than say taste stimulus, we will frequently say _____ stimulus.

gustation

434. The stimulus object in the case of taste or _____ is usually solid or liquid food, such as cake or lemonade.

saliva

435. When food, such as a chocolate bar, is placed in the mouth, it dissolves in the water-like substance of the mouth called SALIVA. When food dissolves in the _____ of the mouth, the food is "chemically broken down."

saliva

gustation/taste

436. When food dissolves in _____, the chemicals in the food are "released." The resulting chemicals are the stimuli for _____.

gustation

437. Because we place a number of different kinds of foods and liquids in the mouth, there is a variety of chemicals released that can activate the sense of _____.

chemicals

438.   The chemical breakdown of food in the saliva of the mouth releases chemicals. These _____ serve as STIMULI for the sense of gustation.

stimulus

439.   When common table salt is placed in the mouth, it dissolves in the saliva. The chemicals that are thus released in solution serve as the _____ for gustation.

gustatory

440.   The tongue contains a large number of TASTE BUDS. Chemicals that serve as _____ stimuli activate taste buds.

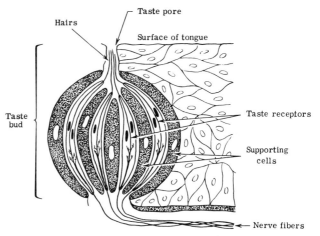

FIGURE 25

Taste

441.   In Figure 25, we see a TASTE BUD. _____ buds are made up of supporting cells and TASTE RECEPTORS.

buds

442.   We are not immediately interested in the supporting cells in the taste _____, but shall concentrate more on the TASTE RECEPTORS that they contain.

taste bud

443.   There are a large number of taste receptors embedded in a single _____ _____.

taste receptors

444.   The taste bud contains a large number of _____ _____.

taste	445. In Figure 25, we can see that there are several HAIRS toward the top of the _____ bud.

taste
buds

446.   These small hairs that come out of the _____ _____ project into a small opening that is called the TASTE PORE.

taste pore

447.   The opening immediately above a taste bud is called the _____ _____.

stimuli

448.   When food goes into solution in the saliva of the mouth, chemicals are released. These chemicals are gustatory _____.

Gustatory

449.   _____ stimuli are chemical in nature.

taste pore

450.   The chemicals contained in the saliva enter the small opening above the taste bud that is called the _____ _____.

taste pore

451.   Once the chemicals in the saliva pass through the _____ _____, they come into contact with taste receptors.

saliva

taste

452.   When the chemicals contained in the _____ of the mouth come in contact with taste receptors, they may activate the _____ receptors.

taste bud

453.   The taste receptors that are embedded within each _____ _____ may be stimulated by the chemicals in the saliva (the gustatory stimuli).

taste receptors

454.   Each taste bud contains a number of taste receptors. Gustatory stimuli may activate the _____ _____ that are within the taste bud.

gustatory
stimuli

455.   Whether or not _____ _____ activate the taste receptors depends on the intensity of those stimuli.

threshold

456. If the combined intensity of all the gustatory stimuli in the mouth is above the absolute _____, then they will excite the taste receptors.

absolute threshold

457. But if the intensity of the gustatory stimuli is below the _____ _____, then the taste receptors will not be activated.

taste
receptors

458. Strictly speaking, gustatory stimuli do not excite the taste bud—they excite the _____ _____within the taste bud.

taste receptors

459. When we say that a taste bud is excited, what we really mean is that the _____ _____ contained within the taste bud are excited.

saliva

460. We have said that food placed into the mouth, be it solid or liquid, dissolves in the _____ of the mouth.

gustatory
stimuli

461. When such food goes into solution, it "chemically breaks down." The chemicals thus released are embedded in saliva and may serve as _____ _____.

taste pore

462. These gustatory stimuli can then go through the small opening called the _____ _____.

gustatory
absolute
threshold

463. If the intensity of these _____ stimuli is above the _____ _____ then the taste receptors will be excited.

taste
receptor

464. If a gustatory stimulus excites a _____ _____, then a nerve impulse is set off.

taste bud

465. If a gustatory stimulus goes through a taste pore it will come in contact with the taste receptors that are embedded in a _____ _____.

absolute
threshold

466. On the assumption that the gustatory stimulus is sufficiently intense, it is above the _____ _____.

taste receptors

467. In this case, the gustatory stimulus will excite the _____ _____.

taste
bud; impulse

468. When the taste receptors in a _____ _____ are excited, a nerve _____ is generated.

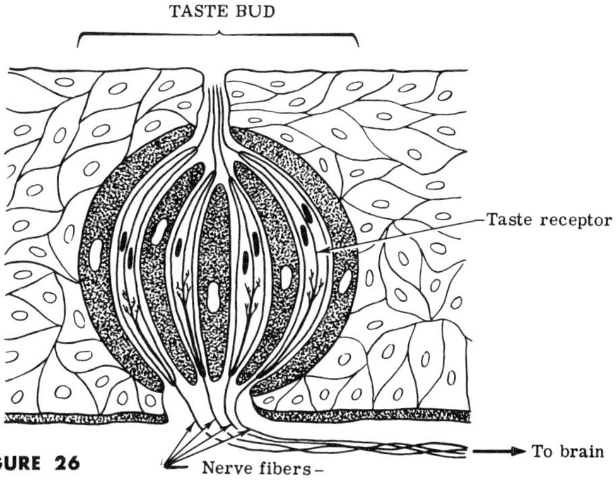

TASTE BUD

Taste receptor

FIGURE 26   Nerve fibers—   To brain

nerve fibers

469. The taste receptors connect to NERVE FIBERS that leave the taste bud in which they are embedded. Figure 26 shows the _____ _____ leaving the taste bud.

nerve fibers

470. When the _____ _____ leave the taste buds, they join three major nerves.

471. These three major nerves are called CRANIAL NERVES. We will not presently be concerned with cranial _____ except to note that they run to the brain.

nerves

472. The cranial nerves will be quite important to us later, at which time we shall consider them in greater detail. For now, we should simply note that the _____ nerves are major nerves that run to the brain.

cranial

473. The important point for us to observe here is that tiny _____ _____ run from the taste buds to join three _____ nerves that run to the _____.

nerve fibers
cranial
brain

474. We can thus see that when the taste receptors are excited, the nerve impulses they produce leave the taste buds and run to the brain by way of three _____ _____.

cranial nerves

475. In the case of audition, vision, and olfaction, nerve impulses run to the _____ by means of a single nerve.

brain

476. Why do gustatory stimuli initiate nerve impulses that run to the _____ by means of three different nerves?

brain

477. In considering this question, note that taste buds are widely distributed throughout the mouth. Thus, _____ _____ are to be found on the upper surface of the tongue, on the roof and the floor of the mouth, in the cheeks, and on the under side of the tongue.

taste buds

478. We do not really know the answer to the question, but we can observe that because taste buds are so widely distributed throughout the mouth, it is difficult for a single nerve to receive nerve impulses from all of them. Considering this wide distribution of taste buds, it seems "more efficient" for three separate nerves to receive _____ _____ from them.

nerve impulses

479. Although _____ _____ may be found in various places in the mouth, they appear mainly on the top or UPPER SURFACE of the TONGUE.

taste buds

480. More taste buds are found on the upper surface of the _____ than in the cheeks.

tongue

upper surface

481. Similarly, more taste buds may be found on the _____ _____ of the tongue than on the roof of the mouth.

tongue

482. We may thus conclude that the upper surface of the _____ is more important for taste than is any other section in the mouth.

taste
buds; upper
surface

483. The reason for this is that _____ _____ appear predominantly on the _____ _____ of the tongue.

cranial nerves
brain

484. The important point for us to note here is that nerve impulses proceed from the taste buds, embedded mainly in the upper surface of the tongue, to three _____ _____ that run to the _____.

saliva

485. Let us now summarize the process of gustation. Event No. 1: When a stimulus object, such as food —be it solid or liquid—enters the mouth, it comes into contact with _____ and goes into solution.

stimuli

486. Event No. 2: When the food goes into solution, chemicals that serve as gustatory _____ are released.

taste pores

487. Event No. 3: These stimuli go through the tiny openings called the _____ _____ that lie next to the taste buds.

gustatory

488. Event No. 4: When these _____ stimuli pass through the taste pores, they come in contact with TASTE RECEPTORS that are embedded in

taste buds

_____ _____.

absolute threshold
taste receptors

489. Event No. 5: If these gustatory stimuli are above the _____ _____, they will excite the _____ _____ that are embedded in the taste buds.

nerve impulses

490.   Event No. 6: When the taste receptors are excited, they set off _____ _____ that leave the taste buds by means of tiny NERVE FIBERS.

nerve fibers

491.   Event No. 7: The nerve impulses are conducted along the tiny _____ _____ to one of three cranial nerves.

cranial
nerves
brain

492.   Event No. 8: The three _____ _____ then conduct the nerve impulses to the _____.

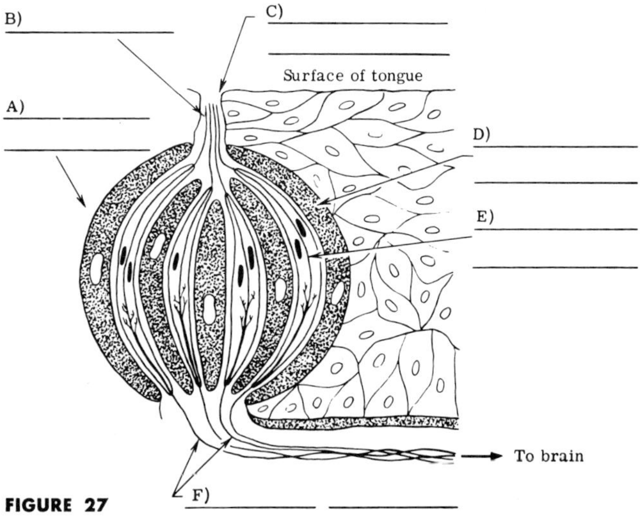

FIGURE 27

493.   Label the parts in the blanks provided in Figure 27.

A. *Taste Bud*
B. *Hairs*
C. *Taste Pore*
D. *Supporting Cell*
E. *Taste Receptor*
F. *Nerve Fibers*

494.   State each step in the process of gustation, from the point at which food enters the mouth, until a nerve impulse is conducted to the brain. Draw a diagram of a taste bud. Then check yourself against the preceding discussion.

RECEPTORS

Section VI: The Cutaneous Senses

senses
495.   We mentioned before that the lay person generally believes that man possesses five senses. These are the _____ of sight, hearing, smell, taste, and touch.

five
496.   We have already covered the first four of the above senses, and shall now turn to the sense of touch. As we take up the sense of touch (the skin senses), we will start to see why we say that man has more than _____ senses.

senses
497.   The word CUTANEOUS ("kŭ tā′nĭ əs") refers to the skin. We shall now consider the four skin senses, or more properly, the four CUTANEOUS _____.

cutaneous/skin
498.   Man has four _____ senses.

cutaneous senses
499.   The four _____ _____ that man possesses are those of PRESSURE, PAIN, COLD, and HEAT.

The Cutaneous Senses
Pressure

cutaneous
senses
500.   We shall consider the _____ _____ in the above order, that is, the pressure sense first, then those of pain, cold, and heat.

501. If you lightly touch a person, you will slightly bend or indent his skin. Such a bending of the *skin* _____ is typically a stimulus for the pressure sense.

skin

502. Bending a person's skin amounts to applying pressure to that person's skin. If the intensity of the pressure is above the absolute _____, it is a stimulus.

threshold

503. The application of pressure to a person's skin is a pressure stimulus, if its _____ is above the absolute threshold.

intensity

504. If you indent or bend a person's skin, we can say that you are applying a pressure _____, provided that its intensity is above the _____ _____.

stimulus
absolute
threshold

505. The part of the skin that we see is only the surface of the skin. Actually, in addition to the surface of the skin, there are several lower layers of *skin* _____.

skin

506. A pressure stimulus, which impinges on a person's skin, will excite receptors embedded in the lower layers of the skin. What are the receptors in the lower layers of the skin for receiving _____ stimuli?

pressure

507. We have good evidence that pressure _____ can activate three different kinds of receptors.

stimuli

508. The three types of receptors that respond to pressure stimuli are known as _____ receptors.

pressure

509. Pressure stimuli may activate three kinds of pressure receptors. The first type of pressure _____ that may receive a pressure stimulus is the BASKET NERVE ENDING.

receptor

510. One type of receptor that responds to pres-
nerve   sure stimuli is the basket _____ ending.

Basket   511. _____ nerve endings are found at the
roots of hairs.

basket nerve   512. These _____ _____ endings are
simply portions of tiny nerves that wrap around the
roots of hairs.

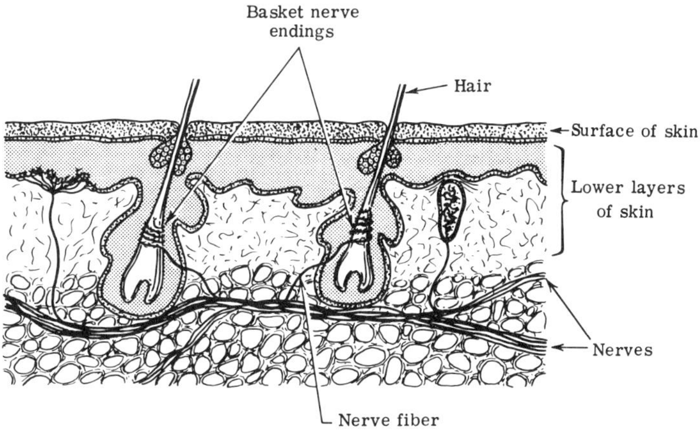

FIGURE 28

513. A diagram of the pressure receptor that is
basket nerve ending   called the _____ _____ _____
is shown in Figure 28.

514. You can see, in Figure 28, that a small nerve
fiber runs from the end of the basket nerve ending.
nerve   This small _____ fiber then goes to a series of
larger nerves.

515. Observe, in Figure 28, how the basket nerve
ending wraps around the roots of the hair. Basket nerve
endings are always found in close conjunction with
hairs   the roots of _____.

516. If the surface of the skin near a hair is bent
or depressed, then the basket nerve ending may be
activated. If a basket nerve ending is activated a
nerve   _____ impulse results.

basket nerve ending

517. The depression of the skin near a hair may activate a _____ _____ _____ to set off a nerve impulse.

activated/excited
nerve impulse

518.   When a basket nerve ending is _____, a _____ _____ results.

basket nerve ending

519. Will any depression of the skin near a hair activate a _____ _____ _____ to set off a nerve impulse?

intensity

520.   The answer is No. The reason for this answer is that the pressure stimulus must be of sufficient _____ (sufficiently "strong") to activate the basket nerve ending.

pressure
absolute threshold

521.   If the bending or depression of the skin produces a _____ stimulus that is above the _____ _____, then the basket nerve ending will be excited.

absolute
threshold; impulse

522.   The activation of a basket nerve ending by a pressure stimulus above the _____ _____ produces a nerve _____.

roots

523.   You will recall that the basket nerve ending wraps around the _____ of a hair. As you would expect, then, if only the hair itself is moved sufficiently, the basket nerve ending will be

activated/excited

_____.

hair

524.   In other words, a basket nerve ending may be excited by touching the skin or by moving a _____.

basket nerve
ending

525.   In either case, if the _____ _____ _____ is activated, a nerve impulse is produced.

nerve impulse
nerve

526.   Once the basket nerve ending produces a _____ _____, that nerve impulse is conducted along the tiny _____ fiber that is shown in Figure 28.

nerve fiber

527.   The nerve impulse is then transmitted along the tiny _____ _____ to larger nerves.

pressure

receptors

528.   The PRESSURE RECEPTORS are widely distributed throughout the skin of the body. Because of this wide distribution, the nerve fibers of these _____ _____ connect to more than just one nerve which conducts nerve impulses to the brain.

nerve impulses

brain

529.   There is a large and complex network of nerves that conduct _____ _____ from the pressure receptors to the _____.

basket nerve

ending

530.   We have said that there are THREE kinds of pressure receptors. The first kind of pressure receptor that we discussed is the _____ _____ _____.

two

531.   The basket nerve ending is the pressure receptor for parts of the skin that contain hairs. Let us now consider the other _____ kinds of pressure receptors.

pressure

receptor

532.   The second kind of _____ _____ that we shall consider is the MEISSNER (Mīz'ner) CORPUSCLE.

corpuscle

533.   The Meissner _____ is embedded in the skin in the hairless regions of the body.

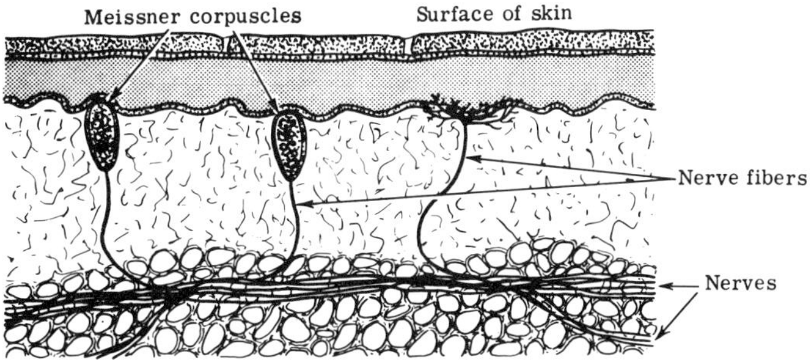

Meissner corpuscles   Surface of skin

Nerve fibers

Nerves

FIGURE 29

Meissner

534.   In Figure 29, you can observe a _____ corpuscle.

535.   If the skin is bent or depressed in a region of the body that lacks hairs, it will probably activate the pressure receptor called the _____

Meissner
corpuscle

_____.

536.   We saw that a tiny nerve fiber is attached to the basket nerve ending. In like manner, a tiny _____

nerve
fiber

_____ is attached to the end of a Meissner corpuscle.

537.   This tiny nerve then joins larger nerves. The network of larger nerves eventually runs to the

brain

_____.

538.   Hence, if a Meissner corpuscle is activated, the

nerve impulse

resulting _____ _____ is transmitted along the tiny nerve fiber to the larger nerves and

brain

then to the _____.

Meissner
corpuscle

539.   The basket nerve ending and the _____ _____ are both activated by pressure stimuli.

540.   In the case of both of these pressure receptors,

nerve impulses
nerve fibers

the resulting _____ _____ are then transmitted along tiny _____ _____

brain

to a series of major nerves and then eventually to the _____.

541.   The basket nerve ending picks up pressure stim-

hairs

uli in regions of the skin that contain _____,

Meissner corpuscle

whereas the _____ _____

pressure

picks up _____ stimuli in the hairless regions of the skin.

pressure
receptor

542.   The third type of _____ _____ is the FREE NERVE ENDING.

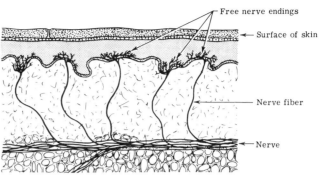

Free nerve endings

Surface of skin

Nerve fiber

Nerve

FIGURE 30

ending

543. As you can see in Figure 30, a free nerve _____ consists of a large number of tiny nerve branches.

free nerve ending

544. Like the basket nerve ending and the Meissner corpuscle, the _____ _____ _____ is activated when the skin is bent or depressed.

nerve fiber

545. Also, like the other two types of pressure receptors, a tiny _____ _____ runs from the end (is actually part) of the free nerve ending.

free nerve ending
nerve impulse

546. When a _____ _____ _____ is activated, a _____ _____ results.

nerve fiber

547. This nerve impulse is conducted along the tiny _____ _____ that runs to a series of larger nerves.

brain

548. By continuing along the larger nerves, the nerve impulse finally enters the _____.

nerve
impulse; brain

549. Let us now summarize the process by which a pressure stimulus produces a _____ _____ that is transmitted to the _____.

bent/indented

550. Event No. 1: When a person's skin is touched, the skin is slightly depressed or _____.

pressure stimulus

551.   Event No. 2: The bending of the skin may be
a _____ _____.

552.   Event No. 3: When a pressure stimulus is applied to the surface of the skin, a pressure receptor

intensity
absolute
threshold

is activated, providing the _____ of
the pressure stimulus is above the _____
_____.

553.   Event No. 4: There are three types of pressure
receptors that can be activated. These are the:

basket nerve ending
Meissner corpuscle
free nerve ending
(different order is
all right)

_____ _____ _____,
_____ _____, and
_____ _____ _____.

pressure
receptor

554.   Event No. 5: The activation of a _____
_____ produces a nerve impulse.

nerve impulse
nerve fiber

555.   Event No. 6: When a nerve impulse is set off by
a pressure receptor, that _____ _____
is conducted along a tiny _____ _____

brain

to a series of larger nerves and thence to the
_____.

556.   Without looking at the preceding discussion,
draw a diagram of each of the three types of pressure receptors, label them, and state the steps from
the point at which a pressure stimulus activates them,
to the point at which a nerve impulse is conducted
toward the brain.

The Cutaneous Senses
Pain

557.   We have now considered the first CUTANEOUS
sense, that of pressure. Let us turn to the second

cutaneous

_____ sense, that of PAIN.

pain 558. In discussing the other senses, we were able to specify a single stimulus, but this is not possible for the sense of _____.

pain 559. The reason for this is that many different stimuli can produce _____.

stimuli 560. Consider the wide variety of _____ that can produce pain. Some examples of PAIN STIMULI are pinching the skin, being hit by a hard object, excessive heat, cuts, and pricks.

Pain 561. The wide variety of stimuli that can produce pain make one point clear: they all can damage the body tissues. _____ stimuli thus help us to survive.

stimuli 562. That is, pain _____ warn us of potential damage to our bodies.

pain 563. There are some people who cannot feel _____. These people are often the victims of serious injury.

stimuli 564. For instance, if a person does not have PAIN RECEPTORS, then he cannot receive pain _____. In this event, he can be seriously burned, cut, or otherwise injured without reacting.

pain 565. In other words, the activation of _____ *receptors* _____ by pain stimuli usually warn us that our body is being damaged.

pain 566. Whenever we feel _____, we immediately react in order to reduce or remove the pain.

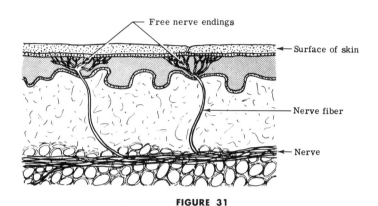

FIGURE 31

567.   In Figure 31, you see a diagram of a free nerve

ending   _____.

nerve   568.   Free _____ endings are embedded in the SKIN and widely distributed throughout the body.

569.   Thus, we do not only feel pain in the skin; we

pain   can also feel _____ in the deeper, or internal parts of the body.

570.   We feel pain in the internal portions of our

free   body when _____ nerve endings in those parts are activated.

571.   A pain stimulus can activate a free nerve ending

receptor   regardless of whether that pain _____ is located in the skin or in the internal parts of the body.

572.   Some organs of the body do not contain

free nerve endings   _____ _____ _____.

573.   For this reason, we cannot feel pain in certain portions of the body. The lungs are an example of an

free nerve   organ that does not contain _____ _____

endings   _____.

pain stimulus   574.   For this reason a _____ _____ applied directly to the lungs fails to produce pain.

nerve impulse

575. If a pain stimulus activates a free nerve ending, then a _____ _____ is set off.

stimulus

576. The pain _____ may be any of a variety such as those that we previously mentioned. For example, acid, thrown on the skin, would prob-

free nerve endings
nerve impulses

ably activate _____ _____ _____ to set off _____ _____.

free
nerve endings

577. Pain stimuli seem to activate _____ _____ _____ by causing them to STRETCH.

stretch

578. When a pain stimulus activates a free nerve ending, it apparently does so by causing it to _____ in a lengthwise ("up and down") direction.

579. When a pain stimulus is applied to the body, there is apparently a lengthwise stretching of

free nerve endings

_____ _____ _____.

nerve fiber
nerves

580. As you can see in Figure 31, the free nerve ending is continuous with a tiny nerve fiber. The tiny _____ _____ is actually part of the free nerve ending that runs to large _____.

activated/stretched
pain stimulus

581. Hence, when a free nerve ending is _____ by a _____ _____, the resulting nerve impulse is conducted along the tiny nerve fiber to large nerves.

brain

582. The nerve impulse is then conducted, by means of a complex set of these large nerves, to the _____.

pain stimuli

583. Let us now summarize what we have said about the sense of pain. Event No. 1: A wide variety of stimuli may produce the feeling of pain. These stimuli are called _____ _____.

free nerve endings

584.   Event No. 2: When pain stimuli are applied to the surface or to the internal portions of the body, they may activate pain receptors which we call _____ _____ _____.

stretch

585.   Event No. 3: These pain stimuli activate free nerve endings by causing them to _____ in a lengthwise fashion.

nerve impulse

586.   Event No. 4: When a free nerve ending is activated, it sets off a _____ _____.

nerve fiber
brain

587.   Event No. 5: When a free nerve ending sets off a nerve impulse, that nerve impulse is conducted along a tiny _____ _____ to a series of large nerves and finally to the _____.

588.   Without looking at the preceding discussion, draw a diagram of a free nerve ending connecting to the larger nerves that run to the brain. State each step that occurs from the point at which a pain stimulus impinges on the organism to where a nerve impulse is conducted toward the brain. Then check yourself against the preceding discussion.

The Cutaneous Senses
Temperature

cutaneous

589.   Because they are embedded in the skin, the TEMPERATURE SENSES are classified along with pressure and pain as _____ senses.

temperature

590.   We are not sure, but there is good reason to believe that there are two different receptors for _____ embedded in the skin.

temperature
receptor

591.   It is likely that one of these is a temperature receptor for heat and one, a _____ _____ for cold.

cold 592. The problem of identifying the receptors for heat and for _____ is an extremely difficult one, and has not yet been solved with a great degree of certainty.

heat
skin 593. There is good reason to believe, however, that the receptors for cold lie near the surface of the skin, whereas the receptors for _____ are embedded in the lower layers of the _____.

heat

cold 594. The receptors for _____ are more deeply embedded in the skin than are the receptors for _____.

receptors 595. We do know that these two different types of temperature _____ are widely distributed throughout the body.

heat
cold
(either order) 596. That is, we can experience _____ and _____ at widely different places in the body.

temperature 597. The temperature of the skin varies between different portions of the body. For example, the temperature in the ear is normally about 82° F., whereas the _____ in the armpit is about 98° F.

temperature 598. The normal _____ of the face and hands is about 90° F.

temperature 599. But the temperature in any given cutaneous (skin) region is usually quite CONSTANT. For example, the _____ of skin of the face is almost always about 90° F.

body 600. We can thus see that the temperature is different for various parts of the _____.

constant 601. But in any given cutaneous region, the temperature is usually quite _____.

602. We know that the stimuli that come from the stimulus objects in our _____ exist at different temperatures. To take an extreme example, the temperature of ice is much lower than that of this book.

environment

603. The word cutaneous refers to the skin. Hence, a region of the skin may be referred to as a _____ region.

cutaneous

604. If a stimulus object, such as a piece of ice, is placed on one cutaneous region of the face, that region becomes _____ than other cutaneous regions of the face.

colder/cooler

605. The piece of ice would, then, lower the temperature of that particular _____ region of the face below its normal 90° F.

cutaneous

606. If a piece of ice is placed on a particular cutaneous region of the face, the cold receptors which lie in the upper surface of that _____ region would be activated to set off _____ _____.

cutaneous
nerve
impulses

607. Any stimulus object that will reduce the temperature of a _____ region by about 2° F. will cause one to feel cold.

cutaneous

608. That is, if a stimulus object changes the temperature of a particular cutaneous region by about 2° F., the cold receptors in that region will be activated to set off _____ _____.

nerve impulses

609. In like manner, any stimulus object applied to a _____ region that is approximately 2° F. HOTTER than that region will activate receptors for _____.

cutaneous

heat

610. Stimulus objects that increase the temperature of a cutaneous region activate heat receptors, while stimulus objects that reduce or decrease the temperature of a cutaneous region activate _____ receptors.

cold

611. That is, if a stimulus object INCREASES the temperature of a cutaneous region by about 2° F., a _____ _____ will be activated.

heat receptor

612. If a stimulus object REDUCES the temperature of a cutaneous region by about 2° F., a _____ _____ will be activated.

cold
receptor

613. When either a cold or a hot stimulus object activates a temperature receptor, a _____ _____ is set off.

nerve
impulse

614. This nerve impulse is then conducted by a series of nerves to the _____.

brain

615. To summarize—Event No. 1: Stimulus objects in our _____ exist at different temperatures.

environment

616. Event No. 2: The surface of the skin in any given region of the body is normally at a constant _____.

temperature

617. Event No. 3: If a HOT stimulus object is applied to a particular cutaneous region, the temperature of that _____ region is _____.

cutaneous
increased/raised

618. Event No. 4: If a hot stimulus object increases the temperature of a cutaneous region by about 2° F., then a _____ receptor is activated. The stimulus, in this event, is above the _____ _____ of the heat receptor.

heat
absolute
threshold

619. Event No. 5: If a heat receptor is activated, a _____ _____ is set off.

nerve impulse

cold receptor

620.   Event No. 6: If a stimulus object is at least 2° F. below the temperature of a cutaneous region, then a _____ _____ is activated to set off a nerve impulse.

cold receptor
nerve impulse
brain

621.   Event No. 7: The activation of either a heat receptor or a _____ _____ sets off a _____ _____ that is conducted to the _____ by means of a series of large nerves.

622.   State each step from the point at which a cold or hot stimulus object is applied to the body, to the point where a nerve impulse is conducted toward the brain, then check yourself against the preceding discussion.

GENERAL SUMMARY OF THE CUTANEOUS SENSES:

pain
temperature

623.   We can thus see that there are four cutaneous senses. One for pressure, one for _____, and two for _____.

four

skin

624.   The _____ cutaneous senses may be activated when stimulus objects impinge on a person's _____.

pressure stimulus

625.   The stimulus that indents or bends the skin is called a _____ _____.

absolute
threshold

626.   If a pressure stimulus is above the _____ _____, it may activate one of three types of pressure receptors.

three
basket nerve endings
Meissner corpuscles
free nerve endings
(different order is
all right)

627.   The _____ types of pressure receptors are: _____ _____ _____, _____ _____, and _____ _____ _____.

pressure
hairs
basket nerve ending

628. The type of _____ receptor found next to the roots of _____ is called the _____ _____ _____.

Meissner
corpuscle

629. The name of the pressure receptor found in hairless regions of the body is the _____ _____.

pressure
nerve
impulse

630. When a pressure receptor is activated, excited, or stimulated by a _____ stimulus from a person's environment, a _____ _____ is generated.

nerve fiber
brain

631. The nerve impulse is then conducted along a tiny _____ _____ to a series of larger nerves and finally to the _____.

cutaneous

632. The second _____ sense that we considered was that for pain.

environment

633. A wide variety of stimuli from a person's _____ may activate the sense of pain.

stimulus

free nerve ending

634. If a pain _____ impinges on an organism, it will excite the pain receptor called a _____ _____ _____.

excites/activates
nerve impulse

635. When a pain stimulus _____ a free nerve ending, a _____ _____ is generated.

nerves

636. The nerve impulse is then conducted along a tiny nerve fiber to a series of large _____, which ultimately deliver the nerve impulse to the

brain

_____.

impinges

637. The same general process occurs in the case of the temperature sense. That is, a stimulus from a person's environment _____ on an organism.

638. If the stimulus is at least 2° F. hotter than the _cutaneous_ _____ region with which it comes in contact, then _____ _heat_ receptors will be excited.

639. But if the stimulus is at least 2° F. colder than the cutaneous region, it will activate _____ _cold_ _____. _receptors_

640. In either case, a _____ _____ _nerve impulse_ is generated that is conducted along a tiny _____ _nerve_ _____ to a series of large _____ _fiber; nerves_ that conduct the impulse to the _____. _brain_

RECEPTORS

Section VII: The Kinesthetic Sense

sense

641. The KINESTHETIC (kĭn əs thĕt′ĭk) SENSE is one of which most people are not aware. This may be because the receptors for the kinesthetic _____ are strictly internal and cannot normally be seen.

kinesthetic

642. Additionally, the kinesthetic sense works almost in an "automatic" fashion. That is, the _____ sense functions regardless of whether or not we "pay attention" to it.

kinesthetic sense

643. But the kinesthetic sense is of extremely great importance to us. For one thing, the _____ _____ "tells" us about the location of our LIMBS in space.

kinesthetic sense

644. Suppose that you close your eyes and place your left arm behind you. You "know" perfectly well where your left arm is in space. This knowledge is due to the functioning of the _____ _____ in that arm.

limbs

645. The sense of KINESTHESIS (kin′es·the′sis) provides information about the location of our _____ in space.

kinesthesis

646. Actually, however, a more important function of the sense of _____ is to help COORDINATE and INTEGRATE behavior.

kinesthesis   647. The sense of _____ is essential for all types of smooth, *integrated* (coordinated) behavior such as walking, driving a car, writing a letter, and pitching a baseball.

648. Behavior that is not well coordinated or INTE-GRATED would be erratic and "jerky." A person who did not walk in a smooth fashion would make jerky movements. Such behavior could not be called co-
integrated   ordinated or _____.

kinesthetic   649. If you did not receive information by means of your _____ sense, you would find that such activities as walking would be extremely difficult, if not impossible.

650. This point is well illustrated in some clinical cases involving syphilis. Individuals in advanced stages, for instance, manifest jerky and erratic move-
integrated   ments. Such lack of coordinated or _____ behavior is due to improper functioning of the kinesthetic sense.

651. In such cases, the only way he can tell where his limbs are is to see them. Hence, such a person walks in a very jerky and uncoordinated fashion. Such lack of integration is due to improper functioning of
kinesthetic   the _____ sense.

652. We can thus see that there are two functions of the kinesthetic sense. One function is to provide in-
location/position   formation about the _____ in space of a person's limb.

function   653. The second _____ is to help
integrate   coordinate and _____ such activities as walking.

654. Like the other senses, there are RECEPTORS for the kinesthetic sense. These receptors are called kines-
receptors   thetic _____.

receptors   655.   Kinesthetic _____ are found in three different places in the body. These are (1) in the muscles, (2) in the tendons, and (3) in the linings of the joints.

kinesthetic   656.   Let us first consider the _____ receptors in the MUSCLES.

muscles   657.   The kinesthetic receptors in the _____ are called MUSCLE SPINDLES.

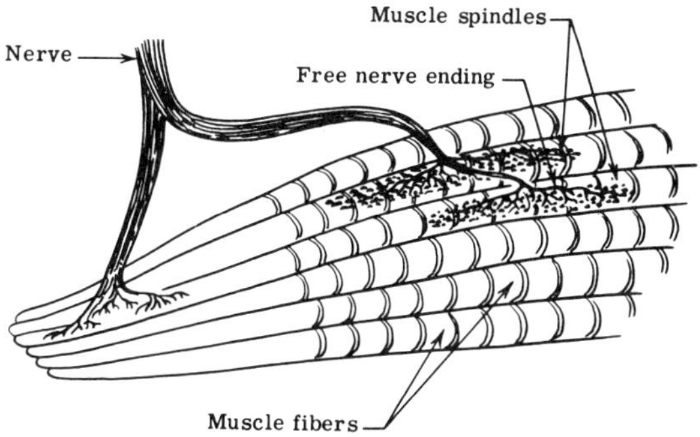

FIGURE 32

            658.   In Figure 32, you see a diagram of a portion of
muscle   a muscle with a _____ spindle.

spindle   659.   The muscle _____ is surrounded by free nerve endings.

            660.   When a muscle is stretched or contracted the
spindle   muscle _____ is activated.

muscle spindle   661.   When a _____ _____ is activated, a nerve impulse is set off.

nerve impulse   662.   The _____ _____ is then transmitted along to the free nerve endings, and then by way of a series of nerves to the brain.

            663.   The kinesthetic receptor that is activated when
muscle   a muscle stretches or CONTRACTS is a _____
spindle   _____.

contracts

muscles/activates

muscle spindles

664. When a person moves his arm, he naturally stretches and _____ the various muscles in it. The contraction and stretching of those _____ provides the stimulus that _____ the kinesthetic receptors (in the muscles) called the _____ _____.

muscle spindles
nerve impulses

665. The activation of the _____ _____ in this manner generates _____ _____ that are transmitted to free nerve endings.

free nerve endings

brain

666. Once a nerve impulse is received by the _____ _____ _____, it is then conducted along to larger nerves and finally reaches the _____.

location/position

667. By thus activating the muscle spindles we receive information about the _____ of our limbs in space.

muscle
spindles

nerve impulses
brain

668. Because we are almost constantly moving the limbs of our body, we are constantly contracting and stretching a large number of muscles. We can thus see that an enormous number of _____ _____ in our muscles are being activated and consequently a very large number of _____ _____ are being transmitted to the _____ from these kinesthetic receptors.

kinesthetic
receptor

669. We have just considered the first type of kinesthetic receptor. The second type of _____ _____ to consider is that embedded in the tendons.

tendons

670. TENDONS are groups of fibers that do not stretch to any appreciable extent. MUSCLES are connected to BONES by means of these groups of fibers called _____.

671. You may think of tendons as being like small but very strong pieces of rope. Tendons connect the

bones   muscles to _____.

muscles   *672.* Tendons are connected to _____ at
bones   one end and to _____ at the other end.
(either order)

673. If a muscle group (such as one in the upper arm) contracts, the forearm (the part of the arm below the elbow) can move up. The reason that the forearm moves up is that the muscles of the upper arm

tendon   pull on the _____ that is attached to the bone of the forearm.

tendons   *674.* When the muscles pull on _____, the bones attached to those tendons move.

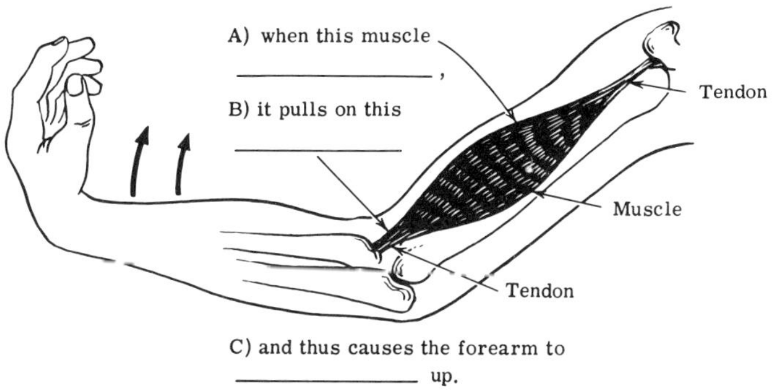

A) when this muscle
_____,
B) it pulls on this
_____
Tendon
Muscle
Tendon
C) and thus causes the forearm to
_____ up.

FIGURE 33

675. In Figure 33, you can see a diagram of this
A. *Contracts*   process. Fill in the blanks provided.
B. *Tendon*
C. *Move, pull,*
   draw, etc.

676. The type of kinesthetic receptor contained in
tendons   _____ is called the GOLGI TENDON ORGAN.

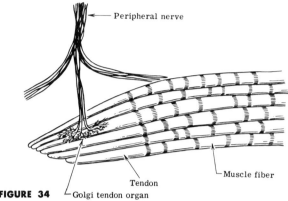

Peripheral nerve

Muscle fiber

Tendon

FIGURE 34 Golgi tendon organ

tendon

677. In Figure 34, we see a diagram of a Golgi _____ organ.

tendon organ

678. As you can see, the tiny nerve fiber of the Golgi _____ _____ connects with larger nerves.

Golgi tendon
nerve impulses

brain

679. Hence, when a _____ _____ organ is activated, _____ _____ are generated and conducted along the tiny nerve fibers to these larger nerves that carry them to the _____.

Golgi tendon
organs

680. When a muscle contracts, it pulls on, or places tension on, the attached tendons. When tension is thus placed on a tendon, the _____ _____ _____ in those tendons may be activated.

threshold

681. Whether or not the Golgi tendon organs are actually excited depends upon whether or not the tension placed on the tendons is above the absolute _____.

tendons

682. When we move our legs, the muscles in those legs contract. The contraction of those muscles places tension on the attached _____.

Golgi tendon organs

nerve impulses

683. When such tension is placed on the tendons, the _____ _____ _____, embedded in those tendons, are activated to set off _____ _____.

kinesthetic

684. The Golgi tendon organ is the second kind of _____ receptor that furnishes us with information about the location of various parts of our body.

Golgi tendon
organs

685. The activation of _____ _____ _____ in the tendons also helps us to manifest smooth, integrated, coordinated behavior.

muscle spindle
tendons

686. The kinesthetic receptor contained in muscles is the _____ _____, whereas the kinesthetic receptor contained in _____ is the Golgi tendon organ.

Golgi tendon
organs
nerve impulses

687. Typically when a muscle contracts, the associated muscle spindles and the _____ _____ _____, in the attached tendons, are activated to set off _____ _____.

kinesthetic
receptor

688. The third type of _____ _____ to consider is that found in the LININGS of the JOINTS.

joint

689. Between the forearm and the upper arm is a JOINT at the point commonly called the elbow. This _____ contains a number of kinesthetic receptors.

joints

690. Essentially, there is a joint at every point in the body where two bones come together. For example, we have _____ at the knee, at the ankle, and in the shoulder.

kinesthetic
receptors

691. We are not really sure what kind of _____ _____ are found in the joints.

joint

692. We do know, however, that whenever a limb moves, the kinesthetic receptors in the linings of the _____ are stimulated.

kinesthetic
receptors

693. The stimulation of the _____ _____ in the linings of the joints tells us something about the relative location of the two bones that meet in the joint.

joints
bones

694. That is, the activation of the kinesthetic receptors in the linings of the _____ informs us that the two _____ that meet in the joint are in a certain location.

lining

695. For example, when we change the location of our upper and lower arms, the kinesthetic receptors in the _____ of the joint, called the elbow, are stimulated.

nerve impulses
brain

696. When these kinesthetic receptors are activated, they generate _____ _____ that are conducted to the _____ by a series of nerves.

muscle spindles
Golgi tendon
organs

linings

697. We have discussed three types of kinesthetic receptors. These are the _____ _____ that lie in the muscles, the _____ _____ _____ that are contained in the tendons, and certain unknown kinesthetic receptors that lie in the _____ of the joints.

free nerve endings

698. We have noticed that free nerve endings are widely distributed throughout the body and we have observed that these _____ _____ _____ can serve a variety of functions.

free nerve endings

699. Although it is not at all certain, it is entirely possible that _____ _____ _____ sometimes also serve as kinesthetic receptors.

kinesthetic
receptor

700. Hence, it may well be that free nerve endings are a fourth type of _____ _____ _____. Let us see why this is so.

701. First let us note that all muscles contain a number of small blood vessels. Blood flows along these blood vessels contained in the _____.

muscles

702. Next, we know that free nerve endings are also contained in muscles. These _____ _____ _____ connect to the blood vessels contained within the _____.

free nerve endings muscles

703. Muscles contain free nerve endings that connect to the numerous _____ _____ that conduct blood.

blood vessels

704. Every blood vessel in the body contains very tiny muscles. Therefore, the blood vessels, embedded in a large muscle themselves, contain tiny _____.

muscles

705. When the tiny muscles in the _____ vessels that are contained in muscle groups contract, it seems likely that they activate the _____ _____ _____ that are attached to them.

blood

free nerve endings

706. When the tiny muscles of the blood vessels contract, they may activate free nerve endings to set off _____ _____.

nerve impulses

707. In some manner, it seems that these free nerve endings are excited by the _____ of the tiny muscles in those blood vessels.

contraction

708. Hence, to be complete, we should note that _____ _____ _____ may also furnish us information about the location of our limbs.

free nerve endings

709. Let us now summarize the functioning of the _____ sense.

kinesthetic

kinesthetic receptors

710. When a portion of the body is in motion, _____ _____ are activated.

activated/excited/
stimulated

711. We know that there are at least three types of kinesthetic receptors that may be _____ when the body moves.

muscle spindles
Golgi tendon organs

joints

712. These three types of kinesthetic receptors are the _____ _____ of the muscles, the _____ _____ _____ of the tendons, and certain unknown receptors in the linings of the _____.

713. In addition, we suspect that there is a fourth type of kinesthetic receptor. We know that muscles contain blood vessels, and that blood vessels themselves contain tiny muscles. This fourth type of kinesthetic receptor is activated when the tiny muscles contained in blood vessels _____.

contract

free nerve ending

714. This fourth possible type of kinesthetic receptor is called the _____ _____ _____.

muscle
spindle; nerve
impulse; brain

715. When a muscle stretches, the kinesthetic receptor in the muscle, called the _____ _____, is activated to set off a _____ _____ that is transmitted to the _____.

tendon

Golgi tendon organs
nerve impulses

716. When a muscle contracts, tension is placed on the attached _____. In this event, the kinesthetic receptors, embedded in the tendons, called the _____ _____ _____, are activated to send off _____ _____.

linings
joints
nerve impulses
brain

717. When the bones that meet in the joints are moved, the kinesthetic receptors in the _____ of those _____ are activated to set off _____ _____ that are eventually conducted to the _____.

location/position

integrated

718. All of these kinesthetic receptors serve to furnish information about the _____ of the various portions of our body and help us to develop smooth, coordinated, _____ behavior.

719. Without looking at the preceding discussion, state each step from the point at which a stimulus impinges on, and thus activates, a kinesthetic receptor, to the point at which a nerve impulse is conducted to the brain. Consider each of the four receptors that we discussed separately, then go back and check yourself against the preceding discussion.

RECEPTORS

Section VIII: The Vestibular Sense

location/position

720. We have just seen that the sense of kinesthesis "tells" us about the movement and the _____ of our limbs in space.

sense

721. Information about movement and position is also furnished by the VESTIBULAR ("věs tĭb'yə lər") SENSE. More specifically, the position of our body in space is furnished us by the vestibular _____.

vestibular

722. The kinesthetic sense informs us of the position of our limbs in space, while the vestibular sense informs us of the general orientation, location or position of our entire body in space. For example, we know that we are right side up instead of upside down due to the functioning of the _____ sense.

kinesthetic

723. If one of your limbs, such as your arm, is placed behind your back, information about its location is furnished by the _____ sense.

vestibular

724. But the information that you are standing right side up, rather than standing on your head, is furnished by the _____ sense.

vestibular
sense

725. If a person closes his eyes, he still has a good idea about the location of his body in space. This information is furnished by the _____ _____.

726. The location of one of your limbs, such as your leg, is furnished by the _____ sense, rather than by the _____ sense.

kinesthetic
vestibular

727. You will recall that the organ for hearing, the cochlea, is located in the inner ear. Other structures are also located in the _____ _____.

inner ear

728. The _____ is the organ for hearing, and it is located in the _____ ear.

cochlea
inner

729. The other structures in the inner ear have nothing to do with hearing, but rather concern the _____ sense.

vestibular

730. There are two general types of organs in the _____ _____ besides the cochlea.

inner ear

731. These are first, the SEMI-CIRCULAR CANALS, second, the UTRICLE and SACCULE. Both the semi-circular canals and the utricle and saccule have to do with the _____ sense.

vestibular

732. The part of the inner ear that has to do with the sense of hearing is the _____.

cochlea

733. The SEMI-CIRCULAR CANALS and the utricle and saccule are also located in the _____ ear.

inner

734. The semi-circular canals and the utricle and saccule, however, have nothing to do with hearing, but they function in connection with the _____ _____.

vestibular sense

735. In studying the vestibular sense, let us first consider the semi-circular _____.

canals

736. There are three _____ canals.

semi-circular

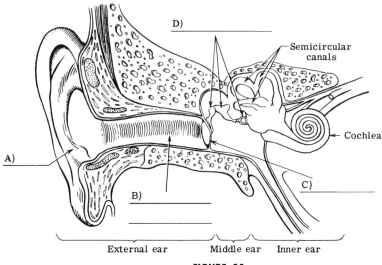

Semicircular
canals

Cochlea

A)

D)

B)

C)

External ear   Middle ear   Inner ear

FIGURE 35

737. In Figure 35, you see a diagram of the external
ear, the middle ear, and the inner ear. Fill in the
blanks.

A. *Pinna*
B. *Auditory canal*
C. *Eardrum*
D. *Ossicles*

738. Note that the semi-circular canals are located
in the _____ _____ directly above the
_____.

inner ear
cochlea

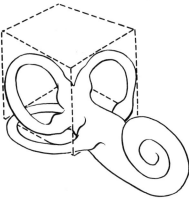

FIGURE 36

739. In Figure 36, you see a larger diagram of the
three _____ _____.

semi-circular canals

planes

740. Now look at the bottom corner of a room. You see that there are THREE PLANES; each plane is perpendicular to the other. That is, the floor is in the horizontal plane, while the two walls, which meet at the corner, are in the vertical planes. The three semi-circular canals roughly correspond to the three _____ that meet in the corner of a room.

semi-circular canals

741. As can be seen in Figure 36, there is a semi-circular canal for the horizontal plane and two _____ _____ for the two vertical planes.

semi-circular canals

742. The three _____ _____ are thus approximately perpendicular to each other.

planes

743. As we shall soon see, the semi-circular canal for each plane furnishes us with information about our movement in each of the three _____.

semi-circular canal

744. Each _____ _____ is filled with a FLUID.

fluid

745. Immersed in the _____ of each semi-circular canal is a set of HAIR CELLS very much like the hair cells in the cochlea.

hair

746. Each semi-circular canal contains a set of _____ cells that is immersed in a fluid.

hair cells
fluid

747. The _____ _____ inside of each semi-circular canal are immersed in _____.

nerve fibers
brain

748. Just as in the cochlea, the hair cells of the semi-circular canals terminate in small nerve fibers. These small _____ _____ connect with the auditory nerve that leads to the _____.

semi-circular
canals

749. When the head is rotated, pressure builds up in the fluid inside the _____ _____.

fluid

750. Rotation of the head increases the pressure of the _____ contained in the semi-circular canals.

hair
cells

751. Because the hair cells inside the semi-circular canals are immersed in fluid, such an increase in pressure of the fluid can affect these _____ _____.

hair
cells

752. An increase in the pressure of the fluid of the semi-circular canals can activate the _____ _____.

pressure

753. The hair cells contained in the semi-circular canals are activated when there is an increase in the _____ of the fluid.

nerve impulses

754. Recall that small nerve fibers leave the ends of the hair cells. The activation of the hair cells generates _____ _____ that run along the small nerve fibers.

nerve

755. The nerve impulses are then conducted to the brain by means of the major nerve called the auditory _____.

auditory

756. Nerve impulses are conducted from the semi-circular canals along the large nerve called the _____ nerve and then to the brain.

fluid

757. Movement of the head, such as occurs in rotation, causes an increase in the pressure of the _____ inside the semi-circular canals.

pressure

758. Such an increase in the _____ of the fluid produces an increase in pressure on the hair cells.

hair
cells

759. This increased pressure on the _____ _____ activates them.

nerve impulses

760. When the hair cells are activated in this manner, they generate _____ _____ that are conducted along tiny nerve fibers.

auditory nerve

761. The impulse then leaves the tiny nerve fibers and runs along the major nerve, called the _____ _____, to the brain.

vestibular

762. Actually, however, it is not the movement or the rotation of the head itself that produces the stimulus for the _____ sense.

stimulus

763. To understand this, observe that when the head is rotated it increases and decreases speed. It is the decreasing or increasing of speed that produces the _____ for the vestibular sense.

decreases

764. Any time one moves his head in any direction he necessarily increases and _____ the speed of its movement.

fluid

765. When one increases or decreases the speed with which he moves his head, he changes the pressure of the _____ within the semi-circular canals.

hair cells

766. Such changes in the pressure of the fluid within the semi-circular canals, then, can activate the _____ _____ to set off nerve impulses.

auditory
brain

767. Nerve impulses generated by the hair cells are then conducted along the tiny nerve fibers to the _____ nerve, and finally to the _____.

vestibular
activated/excited

768. Suppose that you are standing still and start to walk. In this event, the _____ sense will be _____.

not

769. But if the head is moving at a constant speed in a constant direction, you are neither increasing nor decreasing your speed. In this event, the vestibular sense will _____ be activated.

770. In short, any time a person's head increases or decreases speed in any direction (forward, backward, sideways, or in a circular fashion), the

vestibular

_____ sense will be activated—pressure will be produced in the fluid within the

semi-circular canals
hair cells

_____ _____, which in turn activates the _____ _____ to generate nerve impulses.

771. The direction in which we are moving is thus known to us by means of the semi-circular canals of

vestibular

the _____ sense.

772. Let us now turn to the second set of organs in

inner

the _____ ear having to do with the vestibular sense—the UTRICLE (ū′trə kəl) and SACCULE (săk′ūl).

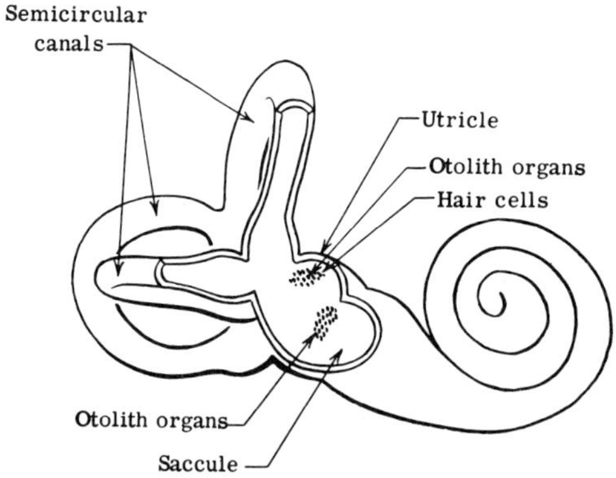

Semicircular canals
Utricle
Otolith organs
Hair cells
Otolith organs
Saccule

FIGURE 37

773. In Figure 37, we see a diagram of the utricle and saccule. These structures contain otolith

organs

_____.

774. Otolith organs look like small stones or crystals.

vestibular

They function in connection with the _____ sense.

775. Inside the two structures called the UTRICLE

otolith

and the SACCULE one finds _____ organs.

776. Inside the utricle and saccule is a kind of fluid or gelatin. Hence, since they are also inside the utricle and saccule, the _____ _____ are embedded in this fluid or gelatin-like substance.

otolith organs

777. In Figure 37, we see that the otolith organs within the utricle and the _____ are close to tiny hair cells.

saccule

778. The tiny _____ cells connect to small nerve fibers which join a larger nerve that runs to the brain.

hair

779. The otolith organs within the saccule and _____ are embedded in a fluid-like substance, and are in close contact with hair cells.

utricle

780. These _____ cells, in turn, connect to small nerve fibers which join a larger nerve. The larger nerve eventually runs to the _____.

hair

brain

781. When there are changes in pressure of the fluid within the saccule and _____, the _____ organs exert pressure against the hair cells.

utricle; otolith

782. When the otolith organs exert pressure on the _____ _____, nerve impulses are generated.

hair cells

783. The nerve impulses are then transmitted to the tiny _____ _____ connected to the hair cells and eventually find their way to the _____.

nerve fibers

brain

784. We can thus see that the following events occur with regard to the utricle and saccule:

785. First, when changes in the pressure of the _____ occur, this change in pressure is exerted against the _____ organs.

fluid/gelatin

otolith

786. Second, when the change in pressure is passed on to the _____ _____, they in turn exert pressure against the hair cells.

otolith organs

787. Third, when the _____ _____ receive the change in pressure from the otolith organs, they are activated to set off _____ _____.

hair cells

nerve impulses

788. The semi-circular canals contain receptors that respond to changes in motion, but the _____ and _____ contain receptors that respond to changes in position of the head.

utricle
saccule

789. For example, if you tilt your head, you change the pressure of the _____ within the utricle and saccule.

fluid/gelatin

790. This change of pressure in the fluid causes the _____ _____ to exert pressure on the hair cells, and _____ _____ are generated.

otolith organs
nerve impulses

791. When you lie down to go to sleep, the events that we have just described "tell" you that your body is in a horizontal _____.

position/plane

792. In an old experiment, the vestibular mechanism, including the utricle and saccule, was removed from a frog. It was then observed that the frog swam upside down about as frequently as he swam right side up. In other words, without the mechanisms within the utricle and saccule, an organism does not "know" what his _____ in space is (unless, of course, he uses other senses such as vision).

position

793. We can thus see that the semi-circular canals have certain functions that are similar to those of the utricle and the _____.

saccule

794. For one thing, the semi-circular canals, and the utricle and saccule, all contain a gelatin or _____.

fluid

795. For another, they all contain tiny receptor cells that are immersed in the fluid. These receptor cells *hair cells* are called _____ _____.

pressure   796. Also, the _____ of the fluid inside them changes with activity of the head.

797. And in each case, as the pressure of the fluid changes, the hair cells are activated, whereupon *nerve impulses* _____ _____ are generated.

798. Furthermore, the nerve impulses generated by the hair cells in both the semi-circular canals and in the utricle and saccule are transmitted from the hair cells along tiny nerve fibers and thence to the brain *auditory nerve* along the _____ _____.

799. In addition to the similarities, however, there are, of course, certain differences. Among these dif- *utricle* ferences is the fact that the _____ and *saccule* _____ contain otolith organs, whereas this is *semi-circular canals* not so for the _____ _____.

semi-circular 800. Furthermore, the _____ *canals* _____ respond to increases and decreases in the speed with which the head moves.

801. Changes in the position of the head, however, *utricle; saccule* activate the _____ and the _____.

802. We thus know when we are increasing and decreasing our speed due to the functioning of the *semi-circular canals* _____ _____, but we know the position of our head in space due to the *utricle* functioning of the _____ and the *saccule* _____.

803. The combined functioning of the semi-circular canals and the utricle and saccule constitute the *vestibular* _____ sense.

vestibular

804. Let us now summarize the above information on the _____ sense.

The Semi-circular Canals:

805. Event No. 1: If the body changes speed of movement in any direction, pressure increases in the fluid within the three _____

semi-circular canals

_____ .

pressure
three

806. Event No. 2: The change of _____ in the fluid within the _____ semi-circular canals informs us of this change of speed in our movement relative to each of the three planes.

hair cells

807. Event No. 3: The pressure changes of the fluid activate _____ _____ that generate nerve impulses.

nerve impulses

808. Event No. 4: The _____ _____ are then conducted along nerve fibers to the auditory nerve.

auditory nerve
brain

809. Event No. 5: The nerve impulses are then conducted along the _____ _____ to the _____ .

The Utricle and Saccule:

utricle; saccule

810. Event No. 1: When the head is tilted, there is a change in pressure of the fluid within the _____ and _____ .

otolith

811. Event No. 2: This change in pressure causes the _____ organs, embedded in the fluid of the utricle and saccule, to exert pressure against hair cells.

hair cells
nerve impulses

812. Event No. 3: Pressure exerted by the otolith organs on the _____ _____ causes _____ _____ to be generated.

813. Event No. 4: The nerve impulses are then conducted along tiny nerve fibers that join the large

auditory nerve ⎯⎯⎯⎯⎯⎯⎯⎯ ⎯⎯⎯⎯⎯⎯.

814. Event No. 5: The nerve impulses are further
brain conducted along the auditory nerve to the ⎯⎯⎯⎯⎯,
position and thus one is informed of the ⎯⎯⎯⎯⎯⎯⎯⎯
of his head in space.

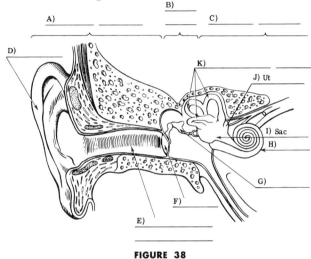

FIGURE 38

815. Label the parts in the blanks provided in Figure
38.

A. *External Ear*

B. *Middle Ear*

C. *Inner Ear*

D. *Pinna*

E. *Auditory Canal*

F. *Eardrum*

G. *Ossicles*

H. *Cochlea*

I. *Saccule*

J. *Utricle*

K. *Semi-circular*
    Canals

816. Without looking at the previous discussion, state
each step by which the vestibular sense informs us of
our movements and position in space.

THE NERVOUS SYSTEMS

Section IX: The Neuron and the Nerve Impulse

receptors

817. You will recall our plan to investigate the biological basis of behavior in three general steps. These were to study the functions of: 1) the receptors, 2) the nervous systems, and 3) the effectors. In the preceding sections we have discussed the first step—how the _____ function.

nerve impulse

818. We have considered ten different receptor processes. In each case we have traced the process by which a stimulus object, or event, activates a receptor to set off a _____ _____ that is conducted to the brain.

activated/
stimulated/excited
brain

819. In this elementary coverage, many interesting matters have necessarily been left for your future study. What we have tried to do is show how the different receptors are _____ to

send nerve impulses to the _____.

nerve
impulses

820. We will now consider how these _____ _____ are transmitted from the receptors through the nervous systems (including the brain and spinal cord) to the effectors.

nerves

821. The NERVOUS SYSTEMS, including the spinal cord and the brain, are composed of NERVES. It now remains for us to be more precise about the nature of these _____ that make up the nervous systems.

nerve

822. Actually a _____ is a very complex structure that is made up of a large number of "tiny nerves" called NEURONS. A nerve is thus a group, or collection, of _____.

neurons

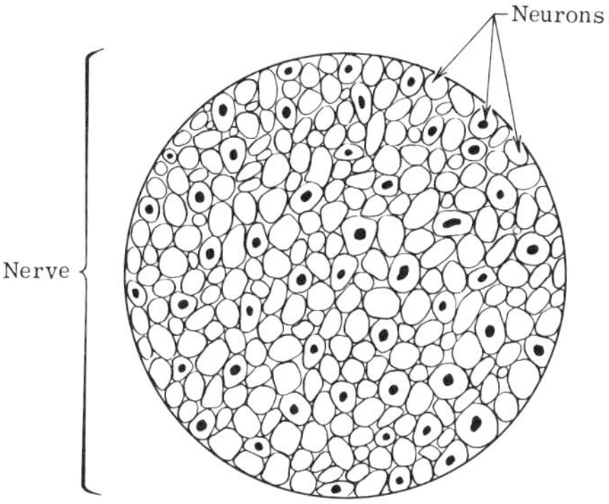

FIGURE 39

823. In Figure 39, we see a cross section of a nerve. You can see that the nerve is made up of a large number of _____.

neurons

824. A nerve is a bundle, group, or collection of "tiny nerves" called _____.

neurons

825. Which is larger: a neuron or a nerve? A _____.

nerve

826. A _____ is larger than a _____.

nerve; neuron

827. We previously said that nerve impulses are conducted along nerves. Now we can be more precise and say that _____ _____ are conducted along the neurons within a nerve.

nerve impulses

828. _____ are tiny nerves that _____ nerve impulses.

Neurons
conduct/transmit

829. A number of nerve impulses can be conducted simultaneously within a given nerve. This is so because each _____ contains a large number of _____.

nerve
neurons

nerve impulses

830.   A nerve impulse is conducted along a neuron that is contained within a nerve. Because each nerve contains a large number of neurons, we can see that a large number of _____ _____ can be conducted within a nerve at any given time.

neuron

831.   It is important for us to study the nature of a nerve impulse that is conducted along a _____ within a nerve.

conducts/transmits

832.   To understand the nature of neural conduction we should study the structure of the neuron, because it is the neuron, itself, that _____ nerve impulses.

absolute threshold
activated/excited

833.   Recall that when a stimulus which is above the _____ _____ impinges on a receptor, that receptor is _____ to set off nerve impulses.

neurons

834.   The nerve impulses so generated are then conducted along _____ within a nerve and usually end up in the brain.

effectors

835.   The nerve impulses are then conducted from the brain to effectors or, more precisely, to one of the two types of _____ called muscles and glands.

brain

836.   Effectors may receive nerve impulses from the _____.

muscles; glands

837.   Once a nerve impulse leaves the brain, it may run to one of the two types of effectors called _____ and _____.

receptor
nerve impulse

838.   We thus have a general overview of neural conduction: When a stimulus impinges on an organism, a _____ is activated whereupon a _____ _____ is generated.

brain

839.   The nerve impulse is then conducted along a series of neurons to the _____.

effectors

840.   Eventually the nerve impulse leaves the brain and runs to one of two types of _____.

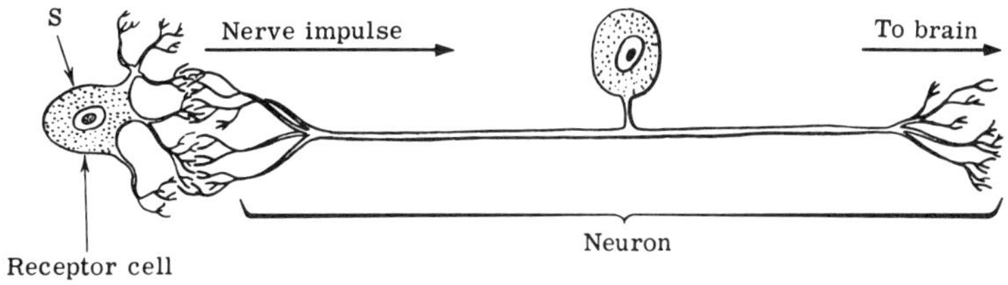

FIGURE 40

receptor

841.   In Figure 40, we see a representation of the first part of this process. The stimulus (S) impinges on a _____ cell, and this action generates a nerve impulse.

neuron; brain

842.   Note, in Figure 40, how the receptor cell connects to, or makes junction with, a neuron. Hence, the nerve impulse is transmitted from the receptor cell to the _____ and then eventually to the _____.

large

843.   Because there are a large number of receptor cells in the organism that make junction with a large number of neurons, and because a large number of stimuli are constantly impinging on the organism, we can see that a _____ number of nerve impulses are constantly being conducted to the brain.

environment

844.   Any organism is constantly being activated by the numerous stimuli in its _____.

neurons

845.   These stimuli are continually activating receptor cells so that numerous nerve impulses are being conducted along the _____ contained within the nerves that run to the brain.

846. Let us now look more closely at the structure of a neuron.

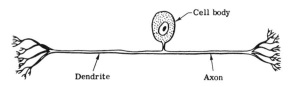

FIGURE 41

847. In Figure 41, we note that there are THREE MAJOR parts of a neuron. These _____ major parts are 1) the CELL BODY, 2) the DENDRITE, and 3) the _____.

three

axon

848. There are _____ parts to each _____.

three

neuron

849. Every neuron has a CELL BODY. It is the _____ body that "feeds" or "nourishes" the neuron and thus "keeps it alive."

cell

850. If a neuron did not have a _____ _____ it would die.

cell

body

851. In addition to the part of the neuron called the _____ _____, every neuron has one or more DENDRITES, and one, but only one, axon.

cell body

852. The dendrite is always on one side of the cell body, whereas the _____ is always on the other side.

axon

853. Although a neuron has more than one dendrite, it can only have one _____.

axon

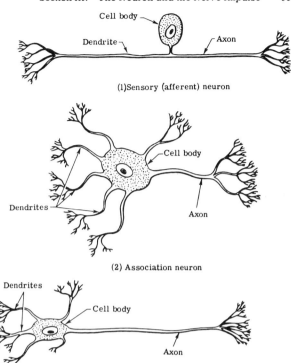

(1) Sensory (afferent) neuron

(2) Association neuron

(3) Motor (efferent) neuron

FIGURE 42

dendrites

854. In every neuron there is one axon, but there may be several ＿＿＿＿＿＿＿＿.

855. Neurons vary considerably in their shape and size. In Figure 42, you can observe three different types of neurons. In each example, note the various arrangements of the axon, the dendrites, and the

cell body

＿＿＿＿ ＿＿＿＿.

856. The neurons that occur in the body may be classified into the three types shown in Figure 42. The first type is the SENSORY, or AFFERENT, neuron, and is typically distinguished by the fact that the ＿＿＿＿

axon

and dendrite are relatively long.

857. Note also, that in the sensory, or afferent, neuron, the cell body projects up from the dendrite

axon

and ＿＿＿＿.

dendrite

afferent

858. The type of neuron in which the axon and _____ are both relatively long, and in which the cell body projects up from them, is known as the sensory or _____ neuron.

dendrite

859. In the afferent neuron, the axon and _____ are quite long.

dendrite; afferent

860. Study Figure 42 and note the long axon and _____ of the sensory, or _____ neuron.

sensory

861. Because it is close to the receptor that receives SENSORY information (stimuli) from the organism's environment, the afferent neuron is also known as the _____ neuron.

afferent/a sensory

862. Hence, when a receptor receives stimulation from the environment, it transmits a nerve impulse to an _____ neuron.

afferent/a sensory

863. The type of neuron that receives a nerve impulse from a receptor, and transmits it TOWARD the spinal cord and brain, is known as an _____ neuron.

toward/to

864. *Af* derives from the Latin, meaning TOWARD, or TO. Hence, afferent neurons conduct nerve impulses _____ the brain.

afferent

865. There are three types of neurons. The type of neuron that conducts nerve impulses toward the brain is called the _____ neuron.

afferent
toward/to

866. When a stimulus object excites a receptor, a nerve impulse is generated. That nerve impulse is then conducted along an _____ neuron _____ the brain.

nerve impulses

three (3)

867. In contrast to the afferent neuron, which conducts _____ _____ toward the brain, there is the MOTOR, or EFFERENT neuron, which is number _____ in Figure 42.

brain

868. Whereas the afferent neuron conducts impulses toward the spinal cord and brain, the efferent, or motor neuron, conducts nerve impulses away from, or out of, the spinal cord and _____.

motor

dendrites

869. In Figure 42, you can see that the efferent or _____ neuron has a number of _____, but only one axon.

efferent

870. Motor, or _____ neurons have a number of dendrites.

axon

871. Like all neurons, EFFERENT neurons have only one _____.

efferent/motor

axon

872. Study the efferent neuron in Figure 42. The dendrites of the _____ neuron are quite short, but the _____ is typically very long.

dendrites

873. In the efferent neuron, the _____ are short.

axon

874. Whereas the dendrites are short in the efferent neuron, the _____ is usually long.

dendrites; axon

875. The efferent neuron usually has several short _____ but a long _____.

long

876. The afferent neuron has a _____ dendrite and axon.

efferent

877. The dendrite of the afferent neuron is typically longer than the dendrites of the _____ neuron.

efferent   878.   The _____ neuron has shorter
afferent   dendrites than the _____ neuron.

878. 879.   The EF of EFferent is derived from the Latin,
efferent/motor;   meaning OUT.   Hence, the _____
neuron   _____ conducts nerve impulses away from, or
out   _____ of, the brain and spinal cord.

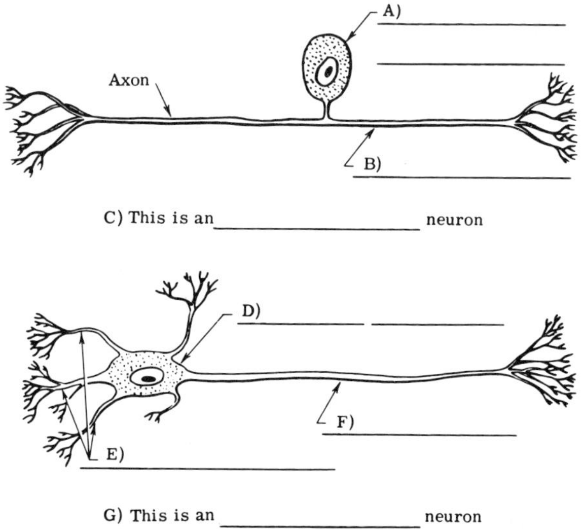

C) This is an _____ neuron

G) This is an _____ neuron

FIGURE 43

880.   In Figure 43, you see two types of neurons.
Write the parts of these neurons, and indicate which
type they are, in the blanks furnished.

A. *Cell Body*
B. *Dendrite*
C. *Afferent/Sensory*
D. *Cell Body*
E. *Dendrites*
F. *Axon*
G. *Efferent/Motor*

881.   Whereas afferent neurons receive nerve (neu-
efferent   ral) impulses from receptors, _____
nerve (neural)   neurons send _____ _____ to
impulses   the muscles and glands.

axon   882.   The efferent neuron has one very long _____
dendrites   and a number of short _____.

cord
muscles; glands

883. Efferent neurons transmit nerve impulses from, or out of, the brain and spinal _____ to the two types of effectors: _____ and _____.

association

884. The third type of neuron found in the body is known as the ASSOCIATION neuron. It is in the BRAIN and SPINAL CORD that we find the _____ neuron.

afferent; efferent
(either order)

885. Refer to Figure 42. As you see, the association neuron is quite different in shape from the _____ and _____ neurons.

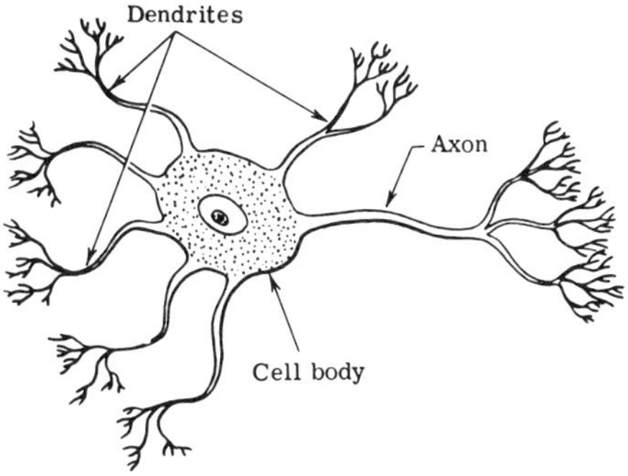

FIGURE 44

association neuron

886. In Figure 44, we see a diagram of an _____ _____.

axon
dendrites;
association

887. As you can see, there is one _____ but a number of _____ in the _____ neuron.

brain; spinal cord

888. Afferent and efferent neurons are found in the body outside of the BRAIN and SPINAL CORD, but association neurons are found only inside, or within the _____ and _____ _____.

association

889. The type of neuron found inside the brain and spinal cord is the _____ neuron.

afferent; efferent

890. On the other hand, the types of neurons found in parts of the body OUTSIDE of the brain and spinal cord are the _____ and _____ neurons.

inside/within
afferent
efferent
(either order)
outside

891. Association neurons are located _____ the brain and spinal cord, whereas _____ and _____ neurons are located in parts

of the body _____ the spinal cord and brain.

nerve
impulses

892. Afferent neurons transmit _____ _____ toward the spinal cord and brain.

association

893. Within the spinal cord and brain we find _____ neurons.

association

894. Therefore, when a nerve impulse leaves an afferent neuron, it is received within the spinal cord, or brain, by an _____ neuron.

toward/to

895. When an afferent neuron transmits a nerve impulse _____ the brain, it is received by an association neuron.

association

896. Nerve impulses are received within the spinal cord and brain by _____ neurons.

association

897. Let us consider one of the simplest possible arrangements of neurons: The case when an afferent neuron transmits a nerve impulse to an association neuron. The _____ neuron, in turn, transmits the impulse to an efferent neuron.

association

898. The three different types of neurons act together. Thus, the afferent and the efferent neurons are linked together, or ASSOCIATED, by means of an _____ neuron.

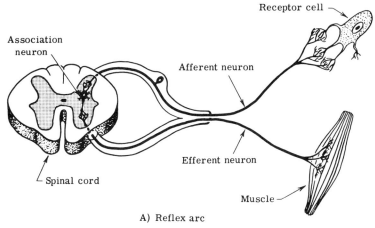

A) Reflex arc

FIGURE 45

899. In Figure 45, we see an example of how these three different types of neurons work together. First, the _____ neuron receives an impulse from a receptor.

afferent

900. This impulse is transmitted from the afferent neuron to an _____ _____ which, in turn, sends the impulse to an efferent neuron.

association neuron

901. When the association neuron transmits the impulse to the _____ neuron, the impulse goes to an effector.

efferent

902. The arrangement of the three neurons, shown in Figure 45, is known as a REFLEX ARC. A series of an afferent neuron, an association neuron, and an efferent neuron, working together to conduct a nerve impulse, is called a _____ arc.

reflex

903. When a nerve impulse is conducted along an afferent neuron into the spinal cord, is received by an association neuron, and conducted out of the spinal cord along an efferent neuron, we have an example of a _____ arc.

reflex

nerve
impulse

904. A simple reflex arc involves the three types of neurons working together to conduct a _____ _____.

reflex arc

905. Actually we have oversimplified this matter, for seldom would we find just a single association neuron in a _____ _____.

association

906. Rather, a number of _____ neurons usually connect an afferent and an efferent neuron to form a _____ _____.

reflex arc

nerve
impulses

907. A reflex arc is a series of neurons that work together to conduct a nerve impulse. For example, if you touch a hot stove, the HEAT and PAIN receptors in your fingers would generate _____ _____.

association
efferent

908. These nerve impulses would then be received by afferent neurons, transmitted to _____ neurons, and then along _____ neurons to effectors.

effectors/muscles

909. When the nerve impulse leaves the efferent neuron and finally arrives at these _____ in your fingers and arms, you withdraw your hand from the hot stove.

reflex arc

910. The activation of a series of neurons that form a _____ _____ requires but a fraction of a second. Think how fast you can withdraw your hand from a hot stove.

effector

911. We thus can see that, in the case of a reflex arc, a neural impulse is very quickly conducted into, through, and back out of the spinal cord to an _____.

nerve impulses

912. We previously said that afferent neurons conduct _____ _____ toward the brain.

913. We thus can see that neural impulses, which enter the spinal cord, can go in two directions: 1) to the brain, and 2) back out of the spinal cord along

efferent   an _____ neuron to an effector.

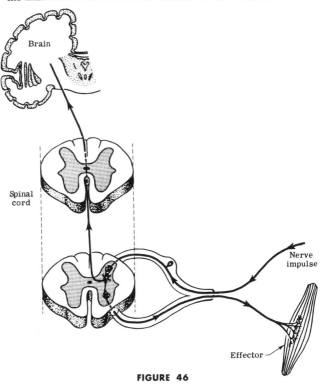

FIGURE 46

914. In Figure 46, we show a reflex arc. You can see that once the neural impulse enters the spinal cord, it may be simultaneously transmitted to an effector

brain   and up the spinal cord to the _____.

915. Neural impulses that enter the spinal cord may go in two directions: 1) up the spinal cord to the

brain   _____, and 2) immediately back out of the

effector   spinal cord to an _____.

916. When a neural impulse is conducted along an afferent neuron, it is referred to as an AFFERENT NEURAL IMPULSE. Hence, an afferent neural impulse

toward/to   is one that is conducted _____ the brain and spinal cord.

917. After an afferent neural impulse enters the spinal cord, it may go in two directions: 1) up the spinal cord into the _____, and 2) back out of the spinal cord along an efferent neuron and finally to an _____.

brain

effector

918. An afferent NEURAL impulse is so named because it is conducted along an afferent neuron. You can now guess that a nerve impulse conducted along an efferent neuron is called an _____ _____ _____.

efferent neural (or nerve) impulse

919. The difference between an afferent and an efferent neural impulse is that the afferent impulse is conducted _____ the brain, whereas an efferent impulse is conducted _____ from the brain.

toward/to

away/out

920. Recall that every neuron has three major parts: the _____ _____, the _____, and the _____.

cell body; dendrites; axon (either order)

921. Think of a reflex arc, and imagine a nerve impulse running along the afferent neuron, then along the _____ neuron, and finally, to the point at which it is transmitted from the association neuron to the _____ neuron.

association

efferent

922. Now focus on the part of the reflex arc where the nerve impulse is transmitted from the association neuron to the _____ neuron.

efferent

923. Which part of the efferent neuron receives the _____ _____?

nerve impulse

924. Does the efferent neuron receive the nerve impulse at its cell body, at its axon, or at its _____?

dendrites

925. The efferent neuron may receive the _____ _____ at either its cell body or at its dendrites.

nerve impulse

926. In general, two parts of a neuron may receive a
nerve impulse. These are 1) the dendrites, and 2) the
cell body. Thus, when a neuron is conducting a nerve
impulse, we know that it received that nerve impulse
cell body   at either its dendrites or at its _____ _____.

927. A neuron may receive a nerve impulse from
either a receptor, or from another neuron. In either
case, that nerve impulse was received by that neuron
cell body; dendrites   at its _____ _____, or at its _____.

928. If a nerve impulse is picked up by the dendrites,
it is conducted past the cell body to the third part of
axon   the neuron called the _____.

929. If the nerve impulse, however, is received directly by the cell body, it is transmitted to the axon,
dendrites   thus bypassing the _____.

930. Whenever a nerve impulse is transmitted along
an axon, it is typically passed on to an effector or to
neuron   another _____.

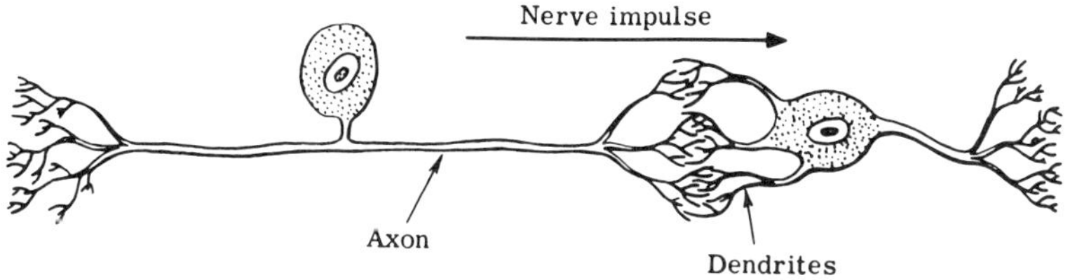

FIGURE 47

931. In Figure 47, we see a representation of a nerve
impulse passing from the axon of one neuron to the
dendrites   _____ of a second neuron.

932. Although a nerve impulse may be received by
cell body   the dendrites, or by the _____ _____ of a
axon   neuron, it is never received by the _____ of a
neuron.

933. In normal functioning, a neuron never receives
axon   a nerve impulse by means of its _____.

axon/cell body

934. Conduction of the nerve impulse is normally in one direction only—from the dendrites toward the _____.

neurons

935. Let us now summarize what we have said to this point. Nerves are bundles of _____.

cell body; axon;
dendrites
(either order)

936. Every neuron has three major parts. These are the _____ _____, the _____ and the _____.

neurons
nerve

937. Nerve impulses are conducted along _____ within a _____.

afferent
association
efferent
(any order)

938. There are three types of neurons within the body. These are the _____ neuron, the _____ neuron, and the _____ neuron.

afferent
neural

939. When a nerve impulse is conducted along an afferent neuron, it is called an _____ _____ impulse.

efferent neural
impulse

940. When an impulse is conducted along an efferent neuron, it is called an _____ _____ _____.

941. When a nerve impulse is transmitted along an afferent neuron, through the spinal cord by means of an association neuron, and back out of the spinal cord along an efferent neuron, we have an example of a

reflex arc

_____ _____.

axons
dendrites
(either order)

942. Afferent neurons have relatively long _____ and _____.

cell body

943. In the afferent neuron, the _____ _____ projects up from the dendrites and axon.

receptors; toward

944. Afferent neurons receive nerve impulses from _____ and conduct them _____ the spinal cord and brain.

afferent

945. Association neurons receive nerve impulses from _____ neurons.

dendrites
cell body

946. The association neuron, like all neurons, receives nerve impulses at its _____ or at its _____ _____ .

axon

947. No neuron ever receives a nerve impulse at its _____ .

association

efferent

948. When a nerve impulse enters the spinal cord, it is received by an _____ neuron, which may then send the impulse to the brain and also out of the spinal cord along an _____ neuron, and then to the effectors.

brain

949. Once a nerve impulse arrives in the spinal cord it may thus go back out to an effector, and also up the spinal cord to the _____ .

dendrites

950. The efferent neuron has only one axon, but a number of _____ .

dendrites; axon

951. The efferent neuron has a number of short _____ , but the _____ is very long.

dendrites; cell body

952. Like all neurons, two parts of an efferent neuron may receive a nerve impulse. These are the _____ and the _____ _____ .

axon

953. An efferent neuron never receives a nerve impulse at its _____ .

nerve impulse

954. With this general understanding, let us now look more closely at how the neuron conducts a _____ _____ .

THE NERVOUS SYSTEMS

Section X: Electrical and Chemical
Aspects of the Nerve Impulse

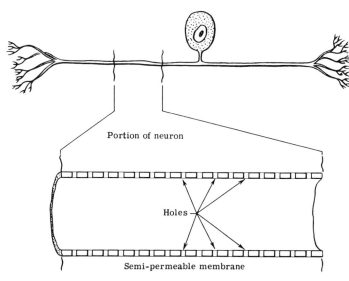

FIGURE 48

955. Consider that we take a portion of a neuron, such as that shown in Figure 48, and magnify it in size. The bottom part of Figure 48 shows that the

neuron _____ has a SEMI-PERMEABLE MEMBRANE.

956. A membrane is a very thin sheet of tissue. The semi-permeable membrane, in Figure 48, is a very thin

neuron sheet of tissue that covers the _____.

957. A membrane covers the outside of a neuron. This

membrane cover is called a semi-permeable _____.

membrane

958. Note the small holes in the bottom of Figure 48. A semi-permeable ———————————————— covers the neuron and has small holes in it.

holes

959. The outside, or cover, of a neuron, called a semi-permeable membrane, has small ———————— in it.

960. Later we shall see why we call this membrane a semi-permeable one. For now, however, simply note that we call the cover of a neuron a

semi-permeable

———————————————— membrane because it has small holes in it.

semi-permeable
membrane

961. Every neuron is covered with a thin sheet of tissue called a ————————————————
——————————————.

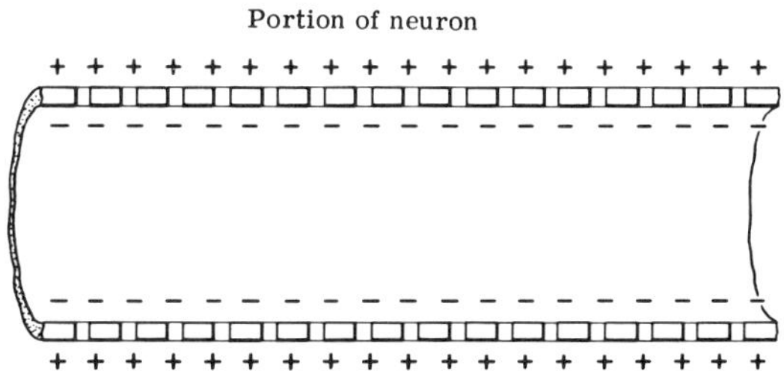

Portion of neuron

FIGURE 49

neuron

962. Figure 49 shows a portion of a ———————— in its normal resting state.

963. Note the small pluses on the outside of the semi-permeable membrane, and the small minuses in-

semi-permeable
membrane

side the ———————————— ————————————.

964. The plus and minus signs stand for IONS (i'ŏnz). An ion is an electrically charged atom. Figure 49 indicates that the neuron has electrically charged atoms

ions

called ————————.

965. The plus signs, in Figure 49, stand for positive ions, and the minus signs stand for negative ions. For

ion

our purposes, we may think of a positive ———————— as an atom with a positive charge of ELECTRICITY.

positive

966. The plus, or positive, signs, in Figure 49, represent _____ ions.

electricity

967. A positive ion is an atom with a plus, or positive, charge of _____.

negative/minus

968. If a positive ion is an atom with a positive charge of electricity, then a negative ion is an atom with a _____ charge of electricity.

positive
semi-permeable

969. In its NORMAL RESTING STATE, the neuron has _____ ions on the outside of its _____ membrane.

semi-permeable
membrane; negative

970. The inside of the _____ _____ has _____ ions.

resting

971. The positive charges of electricity on the outside of the semi-permeable membrane, "balance" (in a sense) the negative charges on the inside. This BALANCE exists when the neuron is in a normal _____ state.

not

972. During the normal resting state of the neuron, the neuron is just "resting"—a nerve impulse is _____ being conducted.

positive
ions
negative ions

973. When a neuron is in its normal resting state, a balance exists between the _____ _____ on the outside of the semi-permeable membrane and the _____ _____ inside the semi-permeable membrane.

positive

electricity; negative
ion

974. An atom that is positively charged with electricity is called a _____ ion, whereas an atom that is negatively charged with _____ is called a _____ _____.

975. The negative ions on the inside of the semi-permeable membrane balance the positive ions on the

outside

state

_____ when the neuron is in its normal resting _____.

976. Let us now see what happens when this

balance

_____ between the positive and negative ions is disturbed.

977. If the neuron is in its normal resting state when a balance exists between the positive and negative

normal

resting state

ions, the neuron stops being in its _____ _____ _____ when that balance is disturbed.

978. The disturbance of the balance between the

outside

negative

ions

positive ions on the _____ of the semi-permeable membrane and the _____ _____ on the inside of the semi-permeable membrane removes the neuron from its normal resting state.

979. When a balance exists between the positive and negative ions, the neuron is in its normal resting

nerve

impulse

state and it, therefore, is not conducting a _____ _____.

980. However, when this balance is disturbed, a

conduct/transmit

neuron starts to _____ a nerve impulse.

981. A nerve impulse starts to be transmitted along

positive

semi-permeable

membrane

negative

a neuron when the balance between the _____ ions on the outside of the _____ _____ cease to balance the _____ ions on the inside.

982. Let us now see more precisely what happens

nerve

impulse

when a neuron conducts a _____ _____.

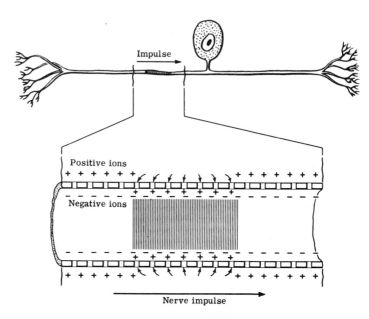

Positive ions

Negative ions

Nerve impulse

FIGURE 50

983.   At the top of Figure 50, the shaded portion of the neuron indicates a nerve impulse traveling along it. A close-up view is shown at the bottom of the figure. The arrows indicate that the _____ ions are moving from the outside to the inside of the semi-permeable membrane.

positive

984.   In other words, when a nerve impulse is conducted along a neuron, positive charges of electricity move through the holes to the inside of the _____   _____.

semi-permeable
membrane

985.   The passage of a nerve impulse along a neuron disturbs the balance between positive and negative ions that exists during the resting state. The disturbance of this balance occurs as the _____ _____ move to the _____ of the semipermeable membrane.

positive
ions; inside

986.   As the nerve impulse moves along the neuron, positive ions continue to move _____.

inside

positive
ions

987.   That is, the movement of positive ions, in one region of the neuron, causes the _____ _____ in the next (neighboring) region to also move inside.

balance

988.   It is the movement of positive ions to the inside of the semi-permeable membrane that disturbs the _____ that exists during the normal resting state.

positive ions

989.   As the nerve impulse moves along the neuron, the balance in each succeeding section of the neuron is disturbed when _____ _____ move inside.

resting state

990.   When a neuron is conducting a nerve impulse, the balance between the positive and negative ions is disturbed, and, at that time, the neuron ceases to be in its normal _____ _____.

cell
body

991.   We previously said that a neuron receives a nerve impulse at its dendrites or at its _____ _____.

resting state

992.   Just prior to the receipt of that nerve impulse, the neuron is in its normal _____ _____.

negative

993.   Let us say that the neuron receives a nerve impulse at its cell body. The entrance of the nerve impulse disturbs the balance in the cell body that exits between the positive and _____ ions in that region of the neuron.

inside

994.   When the balance in the cell body is disturbed, the positive ions start to move to the _____ of the semi-permeable membrane.

positive ions

995. Once the positive ions in the cell body start to move to the inside, this disturbance is passed on to the next region of the neuron. That is, after the positive ions in the cell body move inside, the _____ _____ in the first part of the axon also start to move inside.

inside

996. Eventually, then, all of the rest of the positive ions on the outside of the semi-permeable membrane, in the region of the axon, also move to the _____.

axon

997. In this manner, the nerve impulse that entered at the cell body is conducted through the cell body and along the part of the neuron called the _____.

dendrites

998. Note that when a nerve impulse is received in the cell body, the disturbance of the balance is transmitted directly to the axon, thus by-passing the _____.

axon

999. If, however, the dendrites receive the nerve impulse, it is conducted along the dendrites, through the cell body, and finally along the _____.

semi-permeable membrane

1000. That is, a nerve impulse received at the dendrites causes the positive ions, in all parts of the neuron, to move to the inside of the _____ _____.

electrodes

1001. Let us now study further the electrical aspects of a nerve impulse. Note that an ELECTRODE is essentially a tiny wire. These tiny wires, known as _____, may be inserted into a neuron.

electrodes

1002. Tiny wires inserted into a neuron are called _____.

electrodes

1003. To study the electrical aspects of a nerve impulse the tiny wires, or _____, can then be connected to a VOLTMETER.

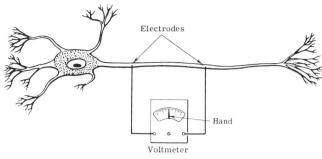

FIGURE 51

voltmeter

1004. A voltmeter is a device that measures amounts of electricity. Note, in Figure 51, that the hand of the _____ is represented by an arrow.

voltmeter

1005. The hand of the _____ moves to indicate the amount of electricity being generated by the nerve impulse.

electrodes

1006. In Figure 51, you can see that two electrodes are inserted into a neuron. A voltmeter is then connected to these two _____.

voltmeter

1007. When a nerve impulse is conducted along a neuron, electricity is generated. The amount of this electricity can be measured by a device called a _____.

nerve impulse

1008. That is, when a _____ _____ flows along a neuron, electricity will flow along the attached electrodes.

voltmeter

1009. When the electricity reaches the voltmeter, it causes the hand of the _____ to move.

hand
nerve
impulse

1010. Thus, by observing the movement of the _____ of the voltmeter, we can measure the amount of electricity generated when a _____ _____ is conducted along a neuron.

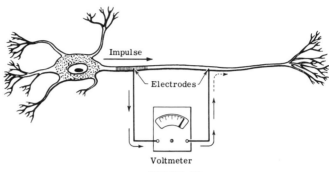

FIGURE 52

1011. Observe, in Figure 52, that when a nerve impulse flows along a neuron, electricity flows along the attached electrodes. When this _____ reaches the voltmeter, it causes the hand of the _____ to move.

electricity

voltmeter

1012. The amount of movement of the hand of the voltmeter indicates how much _____ is flowing through the neuron.

electricity

1013. By recording the movement of the hand, we can measure the amount of electricity generated by the _____ _____ as it moves along the neuron.

nerve impulse

1014. In order to measure the amount of electricity generated by a nerve impulse, we first insert two tiny wires called _____ into a neuron.

electrodes

1015. The electrodes are then attached to a device that measures amount of electricity. This device is called a _____.

voltmeter

1016. As a nerve impulse is conducted along a neuron, the electricity thereby generated will flow through the electrodes and cause the hand on the _____ to move.

voltmeter

1017. The amount of movement of the hand indicates the amount of _____ generated by the nerve impulse.

electricity

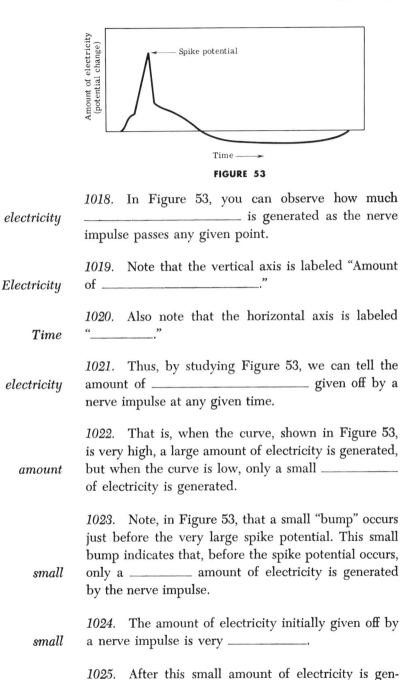

FIGURE 53

electricity
1018. In Figure 53, you can observe how much _____ is generated as the nerve impulse passes any given point.

Electricity
1019. Note that the vertical axis is labeled "Amount of _____."

Time
1020. Also note that the horizontal axis is labeled "_____."

electricity
1021. Thus, by studying Figure 53, we can tell the amount of _____ given off by a nerve impulse at any given time.

amount
1022. That is, when the curve, shown in Figure 53, is very high, a large amount of electricity is generated, but when the curve is low, only a small _____ of electricity is generated.

small
1023. Note, in Figure 53, that a small "bump" occurs just before the very large spike potential. This small bump indicates that, before the spike potential occurs, only a _____ amount of electricity is generated by the nerve impulse.

small
1024. The amount of electricity initially given off by a nerve impulse is very _____.

spike
1025. After this small amount of electricity is generated, the SPIKE POTENTIAL occurs. The _____ potential occurs after an initial small amount of electricity is generated.

potential

1026. As you can see in Figure 53, a very large amount of electricity is given off when the spike _____ occurs.

spike

1027. When the main part of a nerve impulse passes a given point on the neuron, a very large amount of electricity is measured by the voltmeter. This very large amount of electricity is called the _____ potential.

potential

1028. The largest amount of electricity is given off when the spike _____ occurs.

spike potential

1029. Now observe, in Figure 53, that another small bump occurs immediately after the spike potential. After the _____ _____ occurs, an additional, but smaller, amount of electricity is given off.

nerve
impulse

1030. By studying Figure 53, we can thus see how much electricity is generated when a _____ _____ passes any given point on a neuron.

electricity

1031. Thus, when we insert an electrode in a certain point on a neuron, we can measure the amount of _____ given off as the nerve impulse passes that point.

small

1032. When a nerve impulse passes the point at which we have inserted an electrode, at first a very _____ amount of electricity is generated.

spike potential

1033. Next, a very large amount of electricity is then generated. We call this large amount of electricity the _____ _____.

small

1034. Then, immediately following the spike potential, additional electricity flows, but this time it is _____ in amount.

1035. You can thus see that the electrical aspects of a nerve impulse consists of: first, the generation of a small amount of electrical flow, followed by the generation of a major amount, which constitutes the

spike potential _____ _____, following which an additional small amount of electricity flows.

1036. Figure 53 shows what happens when a single nerve impulse is conducted along a neuron. Every nerve impulse gives off one, but only one, spike

potential _____.

1037. Before a neuron conducts or "fires" a nerve

resting impulse, it is in its normal _____ state.

1038. Immediately after a neuron FIRES, it is in an

neuron "exhausted" state. Hence, the _____ needs to recharge itself before it can fire again.

1039. After a neuron conducts a nerve impulse, it is

exhausted in an _____ state and cannot immediately fire again.

1040. Hence, the neuron needs to recharge itself be-

fire fore it can _____ again.

1041. After a neuron conducts a nerve impulse, it starts to recharge itself in order to return to its normal

resting state _____ _____.

1042. The period immediately following the nerve impulse is known as the ABSOLUTE REFRACTORY PERIOD. Immediately after a nerve impulse passes a certain point on a neuron, that point on the neuron enters the

period absolute refractory _____.

refractory *1043.* It is during the absolute _____

period _____ that the neuron is completely unable to conduct a nerve impulse.

absolute
refractory period

1044. No matter how intensely a neuron is stimulated, it cannot fire during the _____ _____ _____.

nerve impulse

1045. After a neuron has conducted a nerve impulse, it is in an exhausted state and enters the absolute refractory period. Before the neuron can conduct another _____ _____ it must recharge itself.

absolute
refractory

1046. It is during the _____ _____ period that the neuron starts to recharge itself.

absolute
refractory period

1047. The absolute refractory period is the first state of recharging. The neuron continues to recharge itself during the RELATIVE refractory period, a period that immediately follows the _____ _____.

nerve impulse

1048. When a neuron is in the absolute refractory period, it absolutely cannot conduct another _____ _____.

refractory
period

1049. But once the neuron leaves the absolute refractory period and enters the relative _____ _____, it is possible to transmit a new nerve impulse.

relative

1050. A neuron CAN fire during the _____ refractory period, provided that the stimulation is greater than normal.

greater/higher

1051. During the relative refractory period the intensity of a new nerve impulse must be _____ than normal in order for it to be conducted by the neuron.

absolute

relative

1052. Although a neuron cannot successfully receive a new nerve impulse when it is in the _____ refractory period, it can when it is in the _____ refractory period, provided that the intensity of the entering impulse is quite high.

recharged

1053. Although the neuron is not completely RE-CHARGED during the absolute refractory period, it is partially _____ during this period.

relative

refractory period

1054. The period immediately following the absolute refractory period is called the _____ _____.

absolute

relative

1055. The _____ refractory period comes before the _____ refractory period.

absolute

refractory period

relative

refractory period

1056. The neuron is absolutely unable to conduct a nerve impulse during the _____ _____, but it can conduct a nerve impulse during the _____ _____, provided that the stimulation is quite intense.

recharges

1057. Once a neuron conducts a nerve impulse, it is exhausted, following which it starts to recharge itself. It is during the absolute and relative refractory periods that the neuron _____ itself.

recharged/

recovered

1058. Following the completion of the relative refractory period, the neuron is returned to its normal resting state and is thus completely _____.

chemical

1059. Although a nerve impulse has ELECTRICAL aspects, it also has CHEMICAL aspects. We have considered some of the electrical characteristics of a nerve impulse, so let us now turn to a brief consideration of some of its _____ characteristics.

semi-permeable

1060.   In the resting neuron, small chemical particles, called SODIUM IONS, exist on the outside of the _____ membrane.

sodium

1061.   You eat sodium ions every day in your table salt. In the resting state the ions that tend to concentrate on the outside of the semi-permeable membrane are called _____ ions.

ions
outside

1062.   When the neuron is at rest, sodium _____ are primarily on the _____ of the semi-permeable membrane.

outside

ions

1063.   Whereas sodium ions are concentrated on the _____ of the semi-permeable membrane, during the resting state, the ions concentrated on the inside are called potassium _____.

inside

1064.   During the resting state, potassium ions are concentrated _____ the semi-permeable membrane.

potassium

1065.   The name of the ion that is concentrated inside the semi-permeable membrane, during the resting state, is the _____ ion.

outside
potassium ions

1066.   In the resting neuron, sodium ions are concentrated _____ the semi-permeable membrane, whereas _____ _____ tend to concentrate inside it.

inside
sodium
ions

1067.   Potassium ions are concentrated _____ the semi-permeable membrane, whereas _____ _____ are concentrated outside.

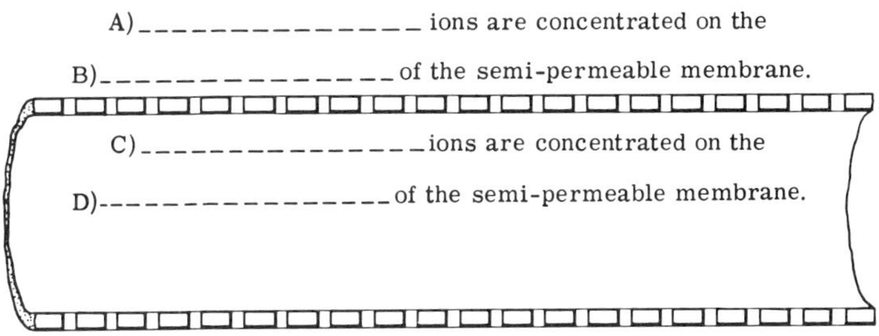

A)_____ ions are concentrated on the

B)_____ of the semi-permeable membrane.

C)_____ions are concentrated on the

D)_____ of the semi-permeable membrane.

FIGURE 54

A. *Sodium*

B. *Outside*

C. *Potassium*

D. *Inside*

1068. In Figure 54, we see a representation of the semi-permeable membrane of a neuron in the resting state. Fill in the blanks.

outside

1069. When a nerve impulse moves along a neuron, the sodium ions move through the small holes from the _____ to the inside of the semi-permeable membrane.

inside

outside

1070. At approximately the same instant that most of the sodium ions have moved to the _____ of the semi-permeable membrane, the potassium ions that are inside begin to move to the _____.

sodium ions

1071. That is, as a nerve impulse moves along a neuron, _____ _____ move to the inside, shortly after which potassium ions start to move to the outside of the semi-permeable membrane.

potassium

ions

1072. It is this passage of sodium ions to the inside of the semi-permeable membrane and _____ _____ to the outside that helps to account for the electrical aspects of a nerve impulse.

sodium

potassium

1073. The electrical aspects of a nerve impulse are largely produced by the passage of _____ ions to the inside, and of _____ ions to the outside of the semi-permeable membrane.

electrical   1074. Both chemical and _____ processes occur during the passage of a nerve impulse.

1075. When the sodium ions come in contact with the potassium ions, certain chemical events occur.
chemical   These _____ events are rather complex and not very well understood.

1076. It has, however, been established that the passage of sodium ions to the inside, and of potassium ions to the outside, produces most of the
electricity   _____ generated by a nerve impulse.

1077. Let us now summarize and extend our discussion of the nerve impulse. A nerve impulse has both
chemical   electrical and _____ aspects.

1078. When a nerve impulse is conducted along a
positive   neuron, _____ charges of electricity
inside   move from the outside to the _____ of the semi-permeable membrane.

1079. We can measure the amount of electricity generated, by attaching electrodes that connect to a
voltmeter   device called a _____.

1080. The chemical aspects of the nerve impulse in-
sodium   volve the movement of _____ ions to the in-
potassium   side, where they come in contact with _____ ions.

1081. As the nerve impulse moves along the neuron,
sodium   at first there is a movement of the _____ ions to the inside, following which there is a move-
outside   ment of potassium ions to the _____.

potassium ions

spike
potential

1082. This movement of the sodium ions to the inside, and of the _____ _____ to the outside, results in the generation of a very large amount of electricity called the _____ _____.

absolute
refractory

1083. The period immediately following the passage of a nerve impulse is called the _____ _____ period.

recharge

1084. During the absolute refractory period the neuron starts to _____ itself.

outside

1085. It is during the absolute refractory period that the sodium ions that have previously moved to the inside, start to return to their original position _____ the semi-permeable membrane.

sodium

1086. During the absolute refractory period, the _____ ions start to return to the outside of the membrane.

relative refractory

1087. This movement of the sodium ions to the outside continues during the period immediately following the absolute refractory period; that is, during the _____ _____ period.

outside

1088. When the relative refractory period has ended, all the sodium ions have returned to the _____ of the membrane.

resting
state

1089. At this point, the balance is restored and the neuron is returned to its normal _____ _____.

nerve
impulse

1090. Once a neuron has been restored to its normal resting state, it is ready to fire another _____ _____.

nerve impulse   1091. Let us say that a _____ _____ is conducted along the neuron and that the neuron is then restored to its normal resting condition.

1092. Suppose that a second nerve impulse is then
neuron   conducted along the _____.

1093. Following this second nerve impulse, the neu-
absolute   ron must, again, go through the _____
refractory   _____ period followed by the
relative refractory   _____ _____ period.

1094. When this second relative refractory period is concluded, the neuron is completely recharged and
normal   is, once again, returned to its _____
resting   _____ state.

1095. You can thus see that this series of events con-
neuron   tinues for as many times as a _____ fires.

1096. We are now in a position to enlarge upon our definition of a semi-permeable membrane. Recall that
semi-permeable   a _____ membrane is a thin sheet of tissue that has tiny holes in it.

1097. When a nerve impulse is conducted, sodium
holes   ions pass through these tiny _____ to the inside of the membrane.

1098. However, in addition to the sodium ions on the
potassium ions   outside, and the _____ _____ on the inside, there are a number of other ions in a neuron.

1099. These various ions are of different size. That is, some are relatively large whereas others are rela-
small   tively _____.

1100. Hence, some ions are too large to get through
semi-permeable   the holes in the _____
membrane   _____.

1101. That is, although sodium ions may pass through the holes to the inside, the holes are too small for other kinds of _____ to pass through.

ions

1102. Similarly, although the holes are large enough to pass potassium ions to the outside, they are sufficiently small to exclude the passage of other kinds of _____ that are present in a neuron.

ions

1103. If all of the various kinds of ions in a neuron could get through the holes, we would have a completely permeable membrane, rather than just a _____ membrane.

semi-permeable

1104. A semi-permeable membrane is one that is large enough to pass some particles, but _____ large enough to allow other particles through.

not

1105. Let us now consider the speed with which a _____ _____ is conducted along a neuron.

nerve impulse

1106. Actually the speed of a nerve impulse varies with the size of the _____ that is conducting it.

neuron

1107. In large neurons, the nerve impulse may travel as fast as 120 meters per second. But, in _____ neurons, it moves as slowly as one meter per second.

small

1108. A nerve impulse travels faster in a _____ neuron than it does in a _____ neuron.

large
small

1109. The greater the diameter of the neuron, the _____ the speed of the nerve impulse.

greater/faster

1110. Or put the other way: the smaller the diameter of the neuron, the _____ the speed of the nerve impulse.

slower/less

1111. Nerve impulses may travel as fast as 120 meters per second in _____ neurons.

large

small

1112. Nerve impulses, however, go as slowly as one meter per second, in _____ neurons.

120

1113. The speed of a nerve impulse varies between approximately one meter per second and _____ meters per second.

faster/greater

1114. The greater the diameter of the neuron, the _____ the speed of the nerve impulse.

axon

1115. Consider, now, a nerve impulse that has been conducted through the cell body and arrives at the end of the neuron called the _____.

axon

1116. What happens to the nerve impulse once it reaches the _____ end of the neuron?

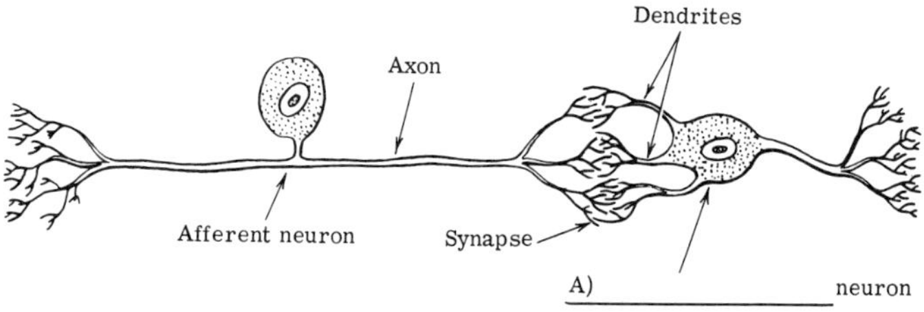

FIGURE 55

A. association

1117. In Figure 55, we see two neurons. The first is an afferent neuron. In the blank provided, write in the name of the second type of neuron.

neurons

1118. A typical arrangement of neurons is shown in Figure 55. Note that the first neuron makes junction with the second neuron, but that the two _____ do not actually touch each other.

dendrites

1119. Observe, in Figure 55, that the axon of the first neuron does not touch the _____ of the second neuron.

neurons

1120. Rather, there is a small space between the two _____ called a synapse (sĭ năps′).

synapse

1121. The small space between two neurons is called a _____.

synapse

1122. How does the nerve impulse cross the _____ in order to get from one neuron to the next?

electrical

1123. Recall that there are both chemical and _____ aspects of a nerve impulse.

nerve impulse

1124. Therefore, we can expect both chemical and electrical events to occur at the synapse between two neurons, in order for the _____ _____ to cross from the first neuron to the second.

synapse

1125. For instance, you have probably seen a spark of electricity jump a gap between two conductors. In like manner, the electrical components of a nerve impulse can "jump" across the _____ between two neurons.

synapse
neuron

1126. Because there are electrical aspects of a nerve impulse, when a nerve impulse reaches the axon end of a neuron, it can "spark," or jump, across the _____ so that the nerve impulse is transmitted to the next _____.

electricity

1127. A nerve impulse may cross a synapse because the _____ that is generated may spark, or jump, across to the next neuron.

nerve impulse

1128. In addition to the electrical events, chemical events also occur when a _____ _____ comes to the end of an axon.

synapse

1129. When the nerve impulse comes to the axon end, certain chemicals are released from the neuron. These chemicals then "float" across the _____ to cause a chemical reaction in the second neuron.

chemical

1130. The release of certain chemicals by the firing neuron produces a _____ reaction in the neighboring neuron.

synapse
reaction

1131. Chemicals released by one neuron cross a _____ and may set off a chemical _____ in the second neuron.

nerve impulse

1132. The resulting chemical reaction, in the second neuron, may then cause that second neuron to fire a _____ _____.

cell body

1133. A second neuron may receive a nerve impulse at one of two places: at its dendrites, or at its _____ _____.

axon
cell body

1134. Therefore, synapses occur between the axon of one neuron and the dendrites of a second, and also between the _____ of one neuron and the _____ _____ of a second.

absolute
threshold

1135. Recall that a stimulus from an organism's environment must be above the _____ _____ before it can excite a receptor.

stimulus

1136. The stimulus from a person's external environment may be thought of as an external _____.

stimulus

1137. In like manner, we may think of a nerve impulse as an internal _____.

synapse

1138. We know that nerve impulses, like external stimuli, differ in intensity. A very intense nerve impulse will release a large amount of electricity to cross a _____ to a second neuron.

small

1139. A weak nerve impulse, however, will only produce a _____ amount of electricity to cross a synapse.

1140. Similarly, an intense nerve impulse will liberate more chemicals to cross a synapse than will a

weak _____ nerve impulse.

1141. The stronger a nerve impulse, the greater the

electricity amount of _____ generated, and

chemicals the greater the amount of _____ liberated.

1142. If the intensity of a nerve impulse is above

absolute threshold the _____ _____, then that nerve impulse will cross the synapse to fire, or excite, the neighboring neuron.

1143. If the nerve impulse is below the

absolute threshold _____ _____, how-

synapse ever, it will not cross the _____ to excite the next neuron.

1144. If a nerve impulse is above the absolute thresh-

synapse old, then it will cross the _____ and be con-

cell ducted along the dendrites, or through the _____

body _____, of the neighboring neuron.

1145. If the cell body receives a nerve impulse, that impulse is conducted through the cell body and along

axon the _____ of the neuron.

1146. If the nerve impulse is below the absolute

not threshold, however, the cell body will _____ receive the nerve impulse.

nerve impulse *1147.* In this event, the _____ _____ simply dies at the synapse.

1148. The cell body and the axon of a neuron have a specific amount of ENERGY that can be released

neuron when the _____ conducts a nerve impulse.

energy

1149. If, in fact, a nerve impulse is conducted through the cell body and axon, all of the _____ of these parts of the neuron is released.

none

1150. If the cell body, on the other hand, does not successfully receive the nerve impulse, then _____ of this energy is released.

all

none

1151. This is known as the ALL OR NONE LAW OF NEURAL CONDUCTION. That is, either the cell body and axon will release _____ of their energy, or they will release _____ of their energy.

All; None

1152. The _____ or _____ Law of Neural Conduction applies to the cell body and axon of a neuron.

cell body

axon

energy

1153. The All or None Law of Neural Conduction states that the _____ _____ and the _____ of a neuron will release all of their _____ or they will not release any of it.

energy

1154. If a nerve impulse goes through the cell body and axon, these parts will release all of their _____.

Neural Conduction

1155. This is known as the All or None Law of _____.

Law

dendrites

1156. Whereas the All or None _____ of Neural Conduction applies to the axon and cell body, it does not apply to the _____.

synapse

energy

1157. That is, if a nerve impulse crosses a _____ to excite a dendrite, the dendrite may release less than all of its _____.

axon

1158. If the dendrite releases all of its energy, then the nerve impulse is conducted right along until it ends up at the _____ end of the neuron.

cell body

1159. If the dendrite, however, releases only a small amount of its energy, then the nerve impulse may die before it reaches the _____ _____ and the axon.

smaller

1160. If a dendrite receives a nerve impulse, it is possible for that nerve impulse to get smaller and _____ as it moves along.

dendrite

1161. If the nerve impulse continues to get smaller as it moves along a _____ of a neuron, it may die.

synapse
dendrite

1162. We can thus see that a nerve impulse may die in either of two places: 1) before it gets to the next neuron at the _____ between two neurons, and 2) at a _____ (part) of a neuron.

nerve impulse

1163. The cell body and the axon act as a unit. If one part receives a _____ _____, then so does the other part.

All
None
dendrites

1164. The cell body and axon obey the _____ or _____ Law of Neural Conduction, but the _____ do not.

axon

1165. If the cell body receives a nerve impulse, then it and the _____ will expend, or fire, all their energy.

All; None
Law; Neural
Conduction

1166. This is known as the _____ or _____ _____ of _____ _____.

1167. This completes our discussion of the neuron and the nerve impulse. Let us now summarize what we have said.

nerve impulse

1168. If a stimulus impinges on one of an organism's receptors, it may excite that receptor. In this event, a _____ _____ is generated.

afferent

1169. The nerve impulse is then received by an _____ neuron.

dendrite
cell body

1170. The afferent neuron, like all neurons, may receive the nerve impulse at its _____ or at its _____ _____.

dendrite
axon
(either order)

1171. In the afferent neuron, the _____ and the _____ are both rather long.

dendrite

1172. The afferent neuron has but one axon and one _____.

cell
body

1173. In the afferent neuron, the _____ _____ projects up from the dendrite and axon.

spinal

1174. Once an afferent neuron receives a nerve impulse from a receptor, the nerve impulse is then conducted into the _____ cord.

association

1175. When the nerve impulse gets to the axon end of the afferent neuron, it may cross the synapse and excite an _____ neuron.

absolute threshold

1176. The association neuron would only receive the impulse if the intensity of the impulse is above the _____ _____.

synapse

1177. If the intensity of the impulse is below the absolute threshold, it would die at the _____ between the two neurons.

cell body

1178. Assume that the association neuron successfully receives the nerve impulse, at either its dendrites, or at its _____ _____.

axon

1179. In this event, the nerve impulse would be conducted through the association neuron until it comes to the end of the neuron called the _____.

efferent

1180. The nerve impulse may then cross the synapse and thus be transmitted out of the spinal cord along an _____ neuron.

effector

1181. Once an efferent neuron receives a nerve impulse, it transmits the nerve impulse to an _____ .

reflex arc

1182. This process of an afferent neural impulse running through the spinal cord and out along an efferent neuron is known as a _____ _____ .

brain

1183. Once a nerve impulse gets inside the spinal cord, however, it not only can go out to an effector, but it can also go up the spinal cord to the _____ .

positive

negatively

1184. In its normal resting state, there are atoms with _____ charges of electricity on the outside of the semi-permeable membrane, and _____ charged ions on the inside.

semi-permeable membrane

1185. When a neuron conducts a nerve impulse, the positive ions move to the inside of the _____ _____ .

chemical
electrical
(either order)

1186. During the passage of a nerve impulse, two types of events occur. These are _____ and _____ aspects of the nerve impulse.

sodium
potassium

1187. The chemical events that occur during the passage of a nerve impulse involve the passage of _____ ions from the outside to the inside of the semi-permeable membrane, and of _____ ions from the inside to the outside.

spike potential

1188. As a nerve impulse passes a given point on a neuron, there is: first, a small amount of electricity generated, followed by a very large amount called a _____ _____ .

small 1189. After the spike potential, another _____ amount of electricity is given off.

absolute 1190. Two periods follow the passage of a nerve
refractory impulse. The first is the _____
relative refractory _____ period, and the second is the
_____ _____ period.

recharges 1191. It is during these two periods that the neuron _____ itself.

outside 1192. While a neuron is recharging itself, the sodium ions return to the _____ of the semi-permeable membrane.

absolute 1193. A neuron cannot receive a new impulse when it is in the _____ refractory period.

relative 1194. It can, however, successfully receive a new
refractory nerve impulse when it is in the _____
_____ period, provided that the intensity of the new impulse is very high.

cell 1195. The All or None Law applies to the _____
body; axon _____ and the _____ parts of a neuron, but
dendrite it does not apply to the _____ part.

all; none 1196. The All or None Law of Neural Conduction states that the cell body and axon will give off either _____ or _____ of their energy.

faster/greater 1197. The greater the diameter of a neuron, the _____ the speed of a nerve impulse that is conducted along it.

synapse 1198. The space between two neurons is called a _____.

THE NERVOUS SYSTEMS

Section XI: The Central Nervous System—The Spinal Cord

neurons

1199. We have said that a nerve is a collection of _____.

neurons

1200. The spinal cord is a much more complex structure than a nerve. Like a nerve, the spinal cord consists of an extremely large number of _____.

neurons

1201. The brain, too, like a nerve and the spinal cord, is also made up of an extremely large number of _____.

spinal cord

1202. A very complex system of neurons make up the brain and _____ _____.

system

1203. The brain and spinal cord work very closely together. It is for this reason that they form a single system called the central nervous _____.

nervous

1204. There are two major divisions of the central _____ system.

central
nervous

1205. The two divisions of the _____ _____ system are the brain and spinal cord.

central nervous
system

1206. The brain and spinal cord make up the _____ _____ _____.

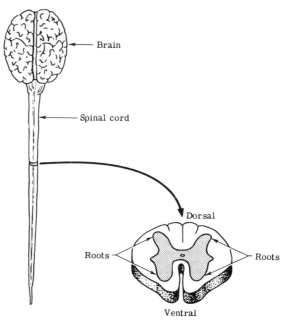

Brain

Spinal cord

Dorsal

Roots

Roots

Ventral

FIGURE 56

brain

spinal cord

1207. In the upper part of Figure 56, we see a diagram of the two parts of the human central nervous system. These two parts are the _____ and the _____ _____.

spinal cord

1208. If the spinal cord were severed, and bent forward toward you, you would see a cross section of it, such as shown in the bottom part of Figure 56. Note the gray matter, in the shape of a butterfly, on the inner part of the _____ _____.

gray

1209. The spinal cord consists of gray matter and white matter. The cross section shows both the white and the _____ matter of the spinal cord.

white matter

1210. The gray matter, in the shape of a butterfly, is on the inside, and the _____ _____ is on the outer parts of the spinal cord.

gray

white

1211. On the inside of the spinal cord one finds _____ matter, whereas in the outer parts one finds _____ matter.

cell
bodies

1212.   Recall the three parts of a neuron. The axons and dendrites are usually white, whereas the _____ _____ of neurons are gray.

white

1213.   Cell bodies of neurons are gray, whereas the axons and dendrites are usually _____ in color.

cell bodies

1214.   Because the inner part of the spinal cord is gray, we know that it could not contain many axons and dendrites. Rather, this butterfly-shaped area primarily contains _____ _____ of neurons.

white

1215.   The outer part of the spinal cord is _____ in color.

axons
dendrites
(either order)

1216.   The outer part of the spinal cord does not consist of cell bodies, but consists mainly of _____ and _____.

gray
white

1217.   With regard to color, in general, cell bodies make up the _____ matter of the spinal cord, whereas axons and dendrites make up its _____ matter.

ventral

1218.   In Figure 56, we have indicated that the back part of the spinal cord is the DORSAL part, whereas the front is the _____ part.

dorsal

1219.   Thus, the ventral part of the spinal cord is toward your stomach, whereas the _____ part is toward your back.

roots/horns

1220.   Note, also, that the gray matter of the spinal cord has four projections called ROOTS, or horns. Study the shape of these four projections called _____.

dorsal roots

1221.   The two roots that project toward the front of the body are called the ventral roots, whereas the two roots that project toward the dorsal (back of the body) are called _____ _____.

cell
bodies

dorsal roots

ventral roots

1222. The gray matter of the spinal cord consists primarily of the parts of neurons called _____ _____ and has four roots: the two that project toward the back of the spinal cord are called the _____ _____, whereas the two that project toward the front of the spinal cord are called _____ _____.

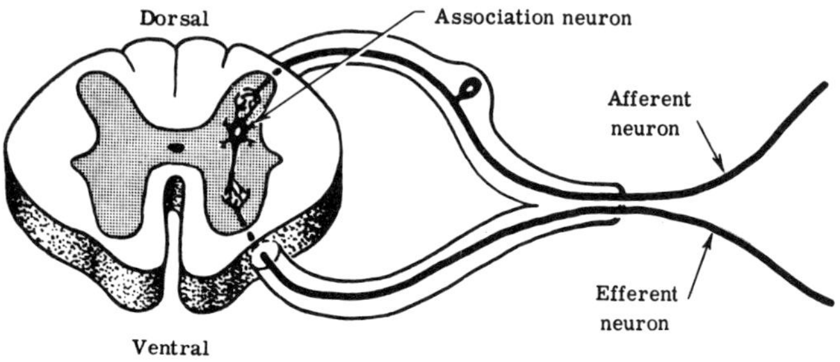

FIGURE 57

association
neuron
efferent neuron

1223. In Figure 57, we show a simple reflex arc. Here, an afferent neuron connects with an _____ _____, which in turn connects with an _____ _____.

gray

1224. Note that the association neuron is contained within the _____ matter of the spinal cord.

cell body

1225. Recalling that the gray matter is made up primarily of cell bodies, we may note that it contains the _____ _____ of the efferent neuron.

Law

1226. On the basis of Figure 57, we can state a famous law known as the Bell-Magendie _____.

dorsal
roots

1227. The first part of the Bell-Magendie Law states that the afferent neurons enter the spinal cord through the roots that we have called the _____ _____. Study this in Figure 57.

afferent

1228. The dorsal roots of the spinal cord receive _____ neural impulses.

Bell   1229.   The _____-Magendie Law has two parts.

Magendie   1230.   The first part: The Bell-_____
afferent   Law states that _____ neurons enter
the dorsal roots of the spinal cord.

1231.   Afferent neural impulses enter the dorsal roots
Bell-   of the spinal cord, according to the _____-
Magendie   _____ Law.

1232.   These impulses are then conducted through the
association neuron to the efferent neuron, then leave
ventral   the spinal cord by means of the _____ roots.

1233.   Hence, the second part of the Bell-Magendie
Law states that efferent neural impulses leave the
ventral   spinal cord by means of the _____ roots.

efferent   1234.   The ventral roots conduct _____
neural impulses out of the spinal cord.

1235.   This   is   the   second   part   of   the   Bell-
Magendie   _____ Law.

1236.   Because efferent neurons exit from the spinal
cord by means of the ventral roots, as shown in
efferent   Figure 57, _____ neural impulses are
conducted   out   of   the   spinal   cord   through   the
ventral   _____ roots.

Bell-Magendie   1237.   Both parts of the _____-_____
afferent   Law stated together are that _____
neural impulses enter the spinal cord through the
dorsal   _____ roots, and efferent neural impulses leave
ventral   the spinal cord through the _____ roots.

1238.   The Englishman, Sir Charles Bell, and the
Frenchman, François Magendie, working independ-
ently, made the discovery that we, today, call the
Bell-Magendie   _____-_____ Law.

afferent

1239. If the dorsal roots of the spinal cord were destroyed, then one could not receive _____ neural impulses.

environment

1240. In this event, a person's spinal cord and brain could not receive sensory information (stimuli) from his _____ for the part of the body affected.

dorsal

1241. A person who could not feel pain in a certain part of his body, for instance, might have a lesion (lē′zhən—a destruction) in his _____ roots.

ventral
roots

1242. In like manner, a lesion in the VENTRAL roots would not allow one to make a response for the region affected. With polio, for instance, a person is paralyzed because the nerve cells in his _____ _____ are destroyed.

neurons

1243. We know that nerves contain neurons. Hence, afferent nerves are made up of afferent _____.

afferent

dorsal

1244. Afferent nerves that contain _____ neurons enter the spinal cord by means of the _____ roots.

efferent

ventral

1245. Efferent nerves contain _____ neurons that leave the spinal cord through the _____ roots.

efferent; spinal

1246. There are a large number of afferent nerves that enter the spinal cord, and a large number of _____ nerves that leave the _____ cord.

spinal nerves

1247. SPINAL NERVES is the name given to these afferent and efferent nerves. All nerves that enter or leave the spinal cord are called _____ _____.

afferent

1248. Afferent neural impulses enter the dorsal roots of the spinal cord by means of _____ neurons.

spinal

1249. These afferent neurons are contained within afferent nerves. The afferent and efferent nerves are called _____ nerves.

spinal cord

1250. Spinal nerves go into and out of the _____ _____.

afferent
efferent

1251. The function of spinal nerves is to deliver _____ neural impulses into the spinal cord and to conduct _____ neural impulses out of the spinal cord.

brain

1252. Let us now see how nerve impulses, once they get into the spinal cord, move up the spinal cord to the _____.

spinal
cord

1253. We will also study how nerve impulses leave the brain and move down the _____ _____.

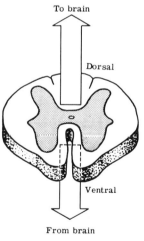

FIGURE 58

dorsal

1254. In Figure 58, note that the ventral and the _____ parts of the spinal cord are labeled.

dorsal

1255. As you can see in Figure 58, nerve impulses are typically conducted up to the brain in the _____ part of the spinal cord.

ventral

1256.   Also note, in Figure 58, that impulses typically are conducted down from the brain along the _____ part of the spinal cord.

dorsal

ventral

1257.   In general, nerve impulses are conducted TO the brain along the _____ part of the spinal cord, and FROM the brain in the _____ part of the spinal cord.

axons

1258.   Recall that the white matter of the spinal cord contains dendrites and _____.

spinal cord

1259.   Many of these axons and dendrites run up and down the _____ _____.

white

1260.   Nerve impulses are conducted up to the brain and down from the brain by means of these dendrites and axons that make up the _____ matter of the spinal cord.

dorsal

dorsal

1261.   Afferent neural impulses that enter through the _____ roots of the spinal cord are conducted to the brain along the axons and dendrites that are in the back, or _____ section, of the spinal cord.

brain

dorsal

1262.   Nerve impulses that enter the spinal cord run to the _____ along neurons contained in the _____ section of the spinal cord.

ventral

1263.   Once nerve impulses leave the brain, they are conducted down the spinal cord along neurons that make up its _____ part.

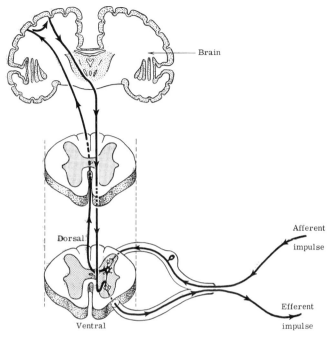

FIGURE 59

afferent

1264. This process is represented in Figure 59. Note how an afferent neural impulse is conducted into the spinal cord by means of an ——————— neuron.

dorsal

1265. The impulse then enters the spinal cord through the ——————— root.

dorsal

1266. It is then conducted up to the brain, in the ——————— section of the spinal cord.

ventral

1267. Once the nerve impulse enters the brain, it sets off a complex of activity. Eventually an impulse descends from the brain and is transmitted along the ——————— section of the spinal cord.

ventral
efferent

1268. The impulse then leaves the spinal cord, through the ——————— roots, and is conducted to an effector by means of an ——————— neuron.

THE NERVOUS SYSTEMS

Section XII: The Central Nervous System—The Brain

brain 1269. Let us now consider, in greater detail, the complex activity that occurs when a nerve impulse ascends the spinal cord and enters the _____.

neurons 1270. We saw that the spinal cord is made up of a large number of neurons. Though it is much more complex in structure, the brain is also made up of a large number of _____.

central nervous 1271. The brain and spinal cord, taken together, make up the central nervous system. Although we shall later consider other nervous systems, for now we are studying the _____ _____ system.

central *nervous system* *brain* 1272. We have already studied the spinal cord, now we will turn to the other part of the _____ _____ _____, that is, we will now study the _____.

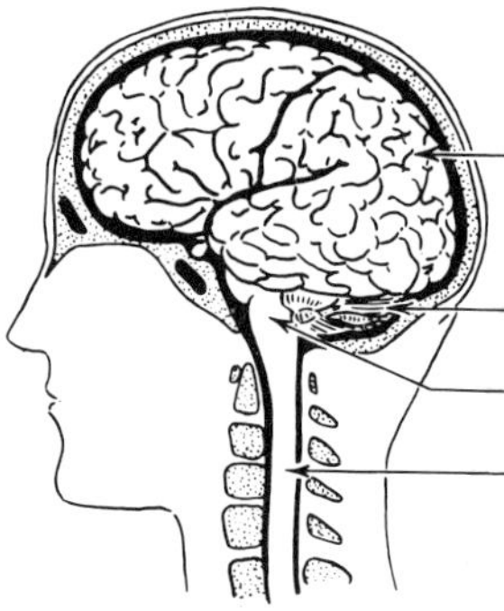

Cerebrum
Cerebellum
Brain stem
Spinal cord

FIGURE 60

brain 1273. In Figure 60, we see a diagram of the upper part of the spinal cord and of several parts of the human brain. Note that as it extends to the brain, the spinal cord runs into the _____ stem.

cerebellum

1274. The other two parts of the brain indicated are the *cerebrum* (sĕr'ə brəm) and the *cerebellum* (sĕr'ə bĕl'əm). The cerebrum constitutes the major part of the brain, whereas the relatively smaller _____ projects below it.

cerebrum
cerebellum

1275. Two major parts of the brain are the cerebrum and the cerebellum. The _____ is larger than the _____.

cerebrum
cerebellum

1276. The larger _____ is above the smaller _____.

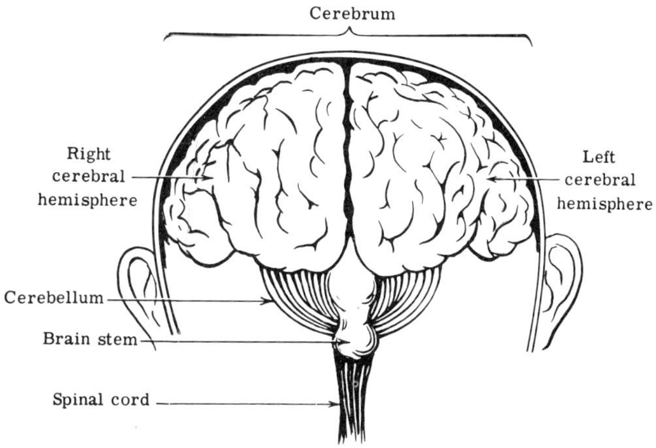

Cerebrum

Right cerebral hemisphere

Left cerebral hemisphere

Cerebellum

Brain stem

Spinal cord

FIGURE 61

cerebrum

1277. In Figure 61, we see a front view of the brain. Most prominent, because it is the largest part of the brain, is the _____.

cerebral hemisphere

1278. Note that the cerebrum is divided into two parts: the left CEREBRAL HEMISPHERE and the right _____ _____.

cerebral

1279. The cerebrum consists of two _____ hemispheres.

cerebellum

1280. Because Figure 61 is a front view of the brain, most of the back part is not shown. For this reason, the structure in the back lower part called the _____ can hardly be seen.

brain

1281. The spinal cord joins the brain at the brain stem. The _____ stem is the lower part of the brain.

brain stem

1282. The spinal cord is joined to the larger part of the brain by means of the _____ _____.

cerebrum

1283. The largest part of the brain is known as the _____.

cerebral hemisphere
right cerebral
hemisphere

1284. There are two major divisions of the cerebrum: the left _____ _____ and the _____ _____ _____.

cerebellum

1285. In the lower back part of the brain, below the cerebrum, one finds a large structure called the _____.

cerebrum

1286. Two cerebral hemispheres make up the _____.

cerebellum

1287. The large sponge-like structure behind and below the cerebrum is the _____.

brain
stem

1288. Between the spinal cord and the cerebrum one finds the lower part of the brain called the _____ _____.

A. *Cerebrum (Right*
Cerebral
Hemisphere)
B. *Cerebellum*
C. *Brain stem*
D. *Spinal cord*

1289. If we sliced the brain down the middle between the two cerebral hemispheres and turned it sideways, we would have a side view of half of the brain, as shown in Figure 62. Fill in the blanks indicated by A, B, C, and D.

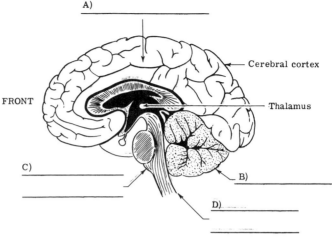

A)

Cerebral cortex

FRONT

Thalamus

C)

B)

D)

FIGURE 62

1290.   Note, in Figure 62, that two other aspects of the brain have been identified—the thalamus and the

cerebral   _____ cortex.

1291.   The thalamus is an internal part of the brain,

cortex   whereas the cerebral _____ is the outer layer of the cerebrum.

1292.   The two new parts of the brain, shown in Figure 62, are the CEREBRAL CORTEX and the THALAMUS. The cerebral cortex is the outer layer of the cerebrum,

thalamus   whereas the _____ is an internal part of the brain.

1293.   Note   the   location   of   the   thalamus.   The

thalamus   _____ is directly above the brain stem.

1294.   Because of its importance, we shall return to the thalamus later. For now, simply note the close relationship   between   the   brain   stem   and   the

thalamus   _____.

1295.   All these parts of the brain are extremely im-

cortex   portant, but the cerebral _____ is especially important.

cerebral cortex

1296. This outer layer of the cerebrum is about ONE-FOURTH INCH in thickness, and is called the _____ _____.

one-fourth/¼

1297. The cerebral cortex is about _____ inch in thickness.

cerebral

1298. Of all the animals, man has the most highly developed _____ cortex.

cell

1299. The cerebral cortex, like the inner butterfly-shaped part of the spinal cord, is composed of the parts of neurons called _____ bodies.

gray

1300. Because it is made up of cell bodies, the cerebral cortex, like the inner part of the spinal cord, is _____ in color.

cell
bodies

1301. Dendrites and axons do not make up the inner part of the spinal cord and the cerebral cortex, but rather, these nervous regions are composed of _____ _____.

gray

1302. Hence, both the spinal cord and the cerebral cortex are _____ in color.

gray

1303. For this reason they are both referred to as _____ matter.

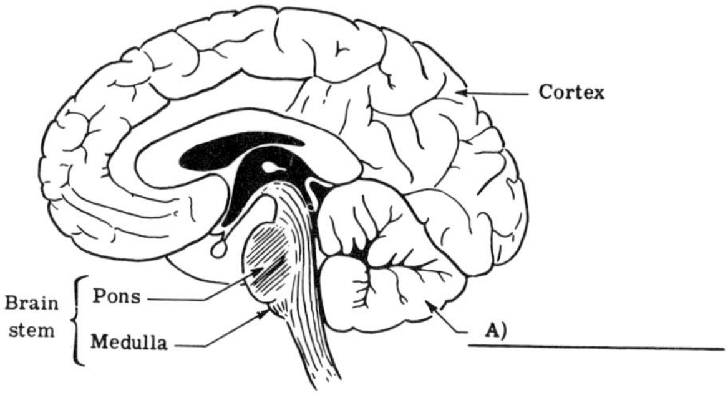

FIGURE 63

A. cerebellum

1304. Identify the part indicated in Figure 63 by filling in the blank.

cerebrum

1305. If we sliced through one of the cerebral hemispheres of the cerebrum, we could see the cerebral cortex. Figure 63 shows the cerebral cortex as the outer layer, or bark, of the major part of the brain called the _____.

cortex

one-fourth/¼

1306. The outer layer of each cerebral hemisphere is called the cerebral _____ and is approximately _____ of an inch thick.

brain stem

1307. Also note, in Figure 63, that the PONS and the medulla are identified as the two major parts of the _____ _____.

spinal
cord

1308. As it enters the brain, the _____ _____ joins the brain stem.

pons

1309. The brain stem consists of two parts: 1) the medulla, and 2) the _____.

brain stem
pons; medulla
(either order)

1310. The lower part of the brain is called the _____ _____, and consists of two parts: the _____ and the _____.

pons

1311. As you can see in Figure 63, the part of the brain stem that is closest to the cerebrum is the _____.

medulla

1312. The part of the brain stem that is closest to the spinal cord is the _____.

pons
medulla

1313. In the brain stem, the _____ is above the _____.

medulla

pons

1314. As nerve impulses ascend the spinal cord and enter the brain stem, they first go through the part of the brain stem called the _____; after which they go through the higher part of the brain stem called the _____.

1315. Man has a large and very highly developed cerebral cortex. It is so large, in fact, that it must fold over in order to fit into the skull, or CRANIUM (krā'-nĭ əm). If the cortex did not fold over, it could not fit into man's _____ .

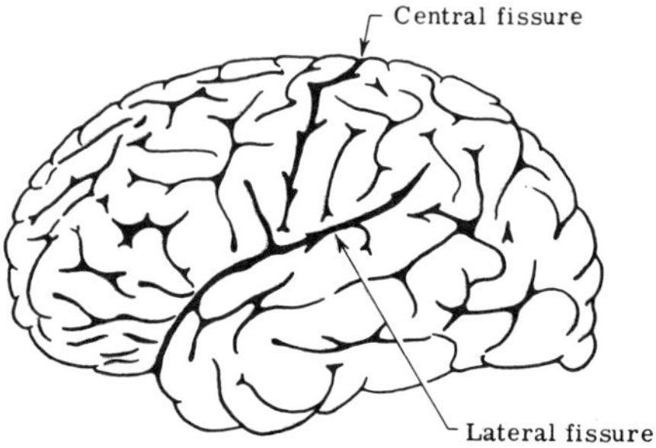

cranium/skull

FRONT

┌ Central fissure

└ Lateral fissure

FIGURE 64

1316. In Figure 64, we show a side view of the cerebrum. The wavy lines indicate folds of the cerebral _____ that allow it to fit into the _____ .

cortex; cranium

1317. If you took a piece of cloth and rumpled it up, it would have many ridges and valleys. The ridges and valleys would look similar to the folds of the cerebral _____ shown in Figure 64.

cortex

1318. These folds, or ridges and valleys, are called CONVOLUTIONS. The _____ cortex has a very large number of convolutions.

cerebral

1319. The wavy lines, in Figure 64, represent the _____ of the brain.

convolutions

1320. Note, in Figure 64, how the numerous folds, called _____, run throughout the entire cerebral cortex.

convolutions

1321. Figure 64 also shows two of the major identifying features of the cortex. One is a vertical groove, or FISSURE (fĭsh'ər) called the central _____ .

fissure

1322. The central fissure is so called because it is in the central part of the cerebrum. Approximately half of the cerebrum is in front of the _____ _____ .

central
fissure

central fissure

1323. The fissure that is in the central part of the brain, and that runs in an up-and-down (vertical) direction, is called the _____ _____.

fissure

1324. As Figure 64 shows, the second major identifying mark of the cortex is the lateral _____.

lateral
fissure

1325. The lateral fissure runs in a lateral, or sidewise, fashion. Note, in Figure 64, that the _____ _____ is directly below the central fissure.

central fissure
lateral fissure
(either order)

1326. The two major fissures of the cortex are the _____ _____ and the _____ _____.

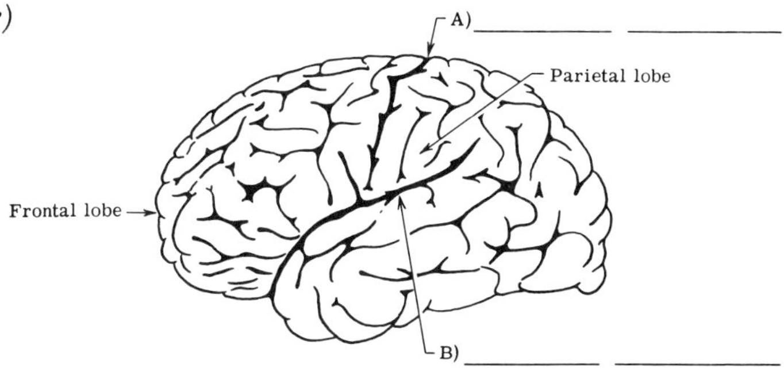

A)_____ _____

Parietal lobe

Frontal lobe →

B)_____ _____

FIGURE 65

A. central fissure
B. lateral fissure

1327. In Figure 65, we see the left cerebral hemisphere. Write the names of the two major fissures in the blanks provided.

four

1328. The lateral and central fissures help to mark off the FOUR major regions of each cerebral hemisphere. These _____ major regions are called LOBES.

back
central

1329. Note, in Figure 65, that the FRONTAL LOBE is in front of the central fissure, whereas the PARIETAL (pə rī′ə təl) LOBE is behind, or in _____ of, the _____ fissure.

frontal lobe

1330. The lobe in front of the central fissure is the _____ _____.

parietal lobe

1331. In back of the central fissure we find the _____ _____.

*cerebral
hemispheres*

1332. The cerebrum consists of two _____ _____.

*right cerebral
hemisphere*

1333. The left cerebral hemisphere is approximately a mirror image of the _____ _____ _____.

*central
lateral
(either order)*

1334. Each cerebral hemisphere is marked off by two major fissures called the _____ fissure and the _____ fissure.

lobes

1335. Each cerebral hemisphere also has four major regions called _____.

frontal

1336. The lobe in the front part of each cerebral hemisphere is called the _____ lobe.

central

1337. The frontal lobe is located in front of the _____ fissure.

parietal

1338. In both the left and right cerebral hemispheres, the _____ lobe is directly behind the central fissure.

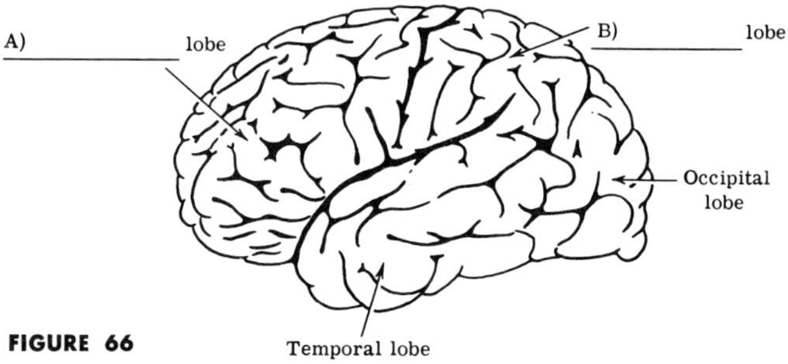

A) _____ lobe   B) _____ lobe

Occipital lobe

FIGURE 66   Temporal lobe

*A. frontal lobe
B. parietal lobe*

1339. In Figure 66, write the names of the two lobes indicated by the blanks.

back/rear

1340. Also note that the *occipital* (ŏk sĭp'ə təl) LOBE is at the very _____ of each cerebral hemisphere.

occipital lobe

1341. The name of the lobe at the rear, or very back, of each cerebral hemisphere is the _____ _____.

occipital

1342. As you can see in Figure 66, the TEMPORAL lobe is below the lateral fissure and in front of the _____ lobe.

temporal lobe

1343. There are two lobes immediately before, or in front of, the occipital lobe. In fact, these two lobes actually connect to the occipital lobe. These are the parietal lobe and the _____ _____.

four

1344. Each cerebral hemisphere contains _____ lobes.

frontal lobe

1345. Immediately in front of the central fissure, one finds the _____ _____.

parietal lobe

1346. Immediately in back of the central fissure is the _____ _____.

occipital lobe

1347. At the very back of each cerebral hemisphere one finds the _____ _____.

temporal lobe

1348. Below the lateral fissure is the _____ _____.

lateral

1349. The temporal lobe is found below the _____ fissure.

central

1350. The parietal lobe is found immediately behind the _____ fissure.

frontal
central

1351. The _____ lobe is found immediately in front of the _____ fissure.

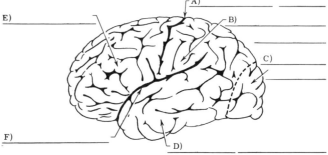

FIGURE 67

1352. In Figure 67, write in the names of the two major fissures and the four lobes of each cerebral hemisphere. If you made any mistakes, you should go back to Frame 1321 and read through the program to this point again.

A. *Central fissure*
B. *Parietal lobe*
C. *Occipital lobe*
D. *Temporal lobe*
E. *Frontal lobe*
F. *Lateral fissure*

1353. Without looking at the preceding discussion, draw a diagram of the left cerebral hemisphere and label the two major fissures and the four lobes. Then check yourself.

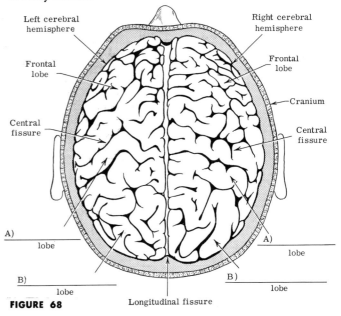

FIGURE 68

1354. In Figure 68, we see a top view of the two
cerebral _____ _____ that
hemispheres compose the cerebrum.

1355. Note that the frontal lobe of each cerebral
central hemisphere is in front of each _____ fissure.

1356. Fill in the names of the lobes, in the blanks
A. *parietal; parietal* provided in Figure 68, for each cerebral hemisphere.
B. *occipital;*
occipital

1357. Note the LONGITUDINAL FISSURE, in Figure 68.
The fissure that divides the cerebrum into two cerebral
longitudinal hemispheres is called the _____
fissure _____.

1358. The right cerebral hemisphere is separated
from the left cerebral hemisphere by means of the
longitudinal _____ _____.
fissure

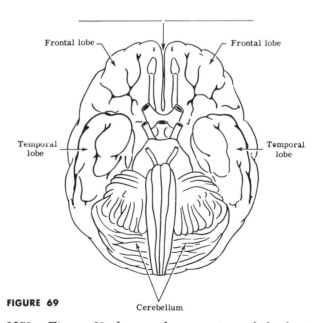

Frontal lobe

Frontal lobe

Temporal
lobe

Temporal
lobe

FIGURE 69   Cerebellum

1359. Figure 69 shows a bottom view of the brain.
Write in the name of the fissure in the blanks pro-
Longitudinal vided.
Fissure

right cerebral hemisphere; longitudinal fissure

1360.   Observe how the left cerebral hemisphere is separated from the _____ _____ _____ by means of the _____ _____.

frontal lobes; temporal lobes

(either order)

1361.   In this bottom view of the brain, the only lobes that you can see are the _____ _____ and the _____ _____ of both cerebral hemispheres.

parietal occipital (either order)

1362.   Observe that you cannot see the _____ lobes and the _____ lobes.

cerebellum

1363.   You could have seen the bottom of the occipital lobes, in Figure 69, had we not hidden them by showing you the _____.

1364.   Let us now review the parts of the brain.

brain stem

1365.   The spinal cord joins the brain at its lower part. This lower part of the brain that connects with the spinal cord is called the _____ _____.

pons; medulla (either order)

1366.   There are two major parts of the brain stem: the _____, and the _____.

pons medulla

1367.   In the brain stem, the _____ is higher than, or above, the _____.

longitudinal fissure

1368.   The cerebrum is the largest part of the brain. It is divided into two cerebral hemispheres by the _____ _____.

cerebellum

1369.   The large sponge-like structure at the lower rear of the cerebrum is called the _____.

four

1370.   The cerebral cortex in each hemisphere is divided into _____ lobes.

frontal

1371. The lobe nearest the forehead and in front of the central fissure is the _____ lobe.

parietal

1372. Immediately behind the central fissure one finds the _____ lobe.

occipital

1373. Located at the very rear of each cerebral hemisphere is the _____ lobe.

lateral

temporal

1374. The lobe in front of the occipital lobe, below the parietal lobe, and directly below the _____ fissure, is called the _____ lobe.

1375. Without looking the the preceding discussion, draw a diagram of the left cerebral hemisphere, the cerebellum, the brain stem, and the spinal cord. Identify the two major fissures that appear in this view of the brain; label each of the four lobes, and show the approximate location of the thalamus. Then go back and check yourself.

THE NERVOUS SYSTEMS

Section XIII: Neural Activity and the
Central Nervous System

afferent

1376. Let us now follow the path of a nerve impulse and focus particularly on what happens to it when it enters the brain. When a receptor is activated, it generates an ＿＿＿＿＿＿＿ neural impulse.

spinal

1377. The afferent neural impulse is then conducted within an afferent (spinal) nerve into the ＿＿＿＿＿ cord.

dorsal

1378. The afferent neural impulse enters the spinal cord by means of its ＿＿＿＿＿ root.

dorsal

1379. It then, typically, moves up the spinal cord along its back, or ＿＿＿＿＿ section.

receptors

1380. As we previously saw, the numerous afferent nerves that enter the dorsal root of the spinal cord are constantly conducting impulses that were generated by ＿＿＿＿＿＿＿ distributed throughout the body.

afferent
neural impulse

1381. Afferent neural impulses that enter the spinal cord by means of spinal nerves come from various places in the body of the organism. For instance, if someone pinched your foot, an ＿＿＿＿＿＿＿＿＿ ＿＿＿＿＿ ＿＿＿＿＿ would be conducted from the foot into the spinal cord.

1382. Not all afferent neural impulses from the body enter the spinal cord; certain others go directly to the brain. All afferent nerves which do not enter the spinal cord go directly to the _____.

brain

1383. The OPTIC nerve originates in the eye. The _____ nerve is an example of a nerve that does not enter the spinal cord.

optic

1384. Rather, the _____ nerve goes directly to the brain.

optic

1385. An afferent neural impulse from the eye does not go to the _____ _____, but rather, it directly enters the brain.

spinal cord

1386. We previously mentioned CRANIAL (krā′nĭ əl) NERVES. _____ nerves go directly to the brain.

Cranial

1387. Instead of entering the spinal cord, _____ nerves go directly to the brain.

cranial

1388. The optic nerve is one of the twelve cranial nerves that directly enter the brain, thus bypassing the _____ _____.

spinal cord

1389. Because they are contained within the cranium, these nerves, which go directly to the brain, are called _____ nerves.

cranial

1390. The auditory nerve, which carries nerve impulses from the ear, is another of the twelve _____ nerves that directly enter the brain.

cranial

1391. The olfactory nerve carries afferent neural impulses generated by the _____ receptors.

olfactory

1392. The olfactory nerve is another of the twelve _____ _____.

cranial nerves

brain; spinal cord

1393. The brain stem is the lower part of the _____ that extends down into the _____ _____.

brain stem

1394. We previously saw that all nerve impulses that ascend the spinal cord enter the lower part of the brain called the _____ _____.

cranial

1395. We have also seen that all afferent neural impulses that come from _____ nerves directly enter the brain.

brain

1396. Most of the cranial nerves enter the lower part of the brain called the _____ stem.

cranial

brain stem

1397. We can thus see that most of the afferent neural impulses, whether they come from spinal nerves and ascend the spinal cord, or whether they come from _____ nerves, enter the lower part of the brain called the _____ _____.

spinal

1398. Every afferent neural impulse that enters the spinal cord crosses over to the opposite side of the _____ cord.

cerebral

1399. Once a nerve impulse crosses to the opposite side of the spinal cord, it eventually enters the _____ hemisphere on that side of the body.

cerebral hemisphere

1400. For example, if a nerve impulse enters the spinal cord from the left side of the body, it crosses to the right side of the spinal cord and eventually goes to the right side of the cerebrum, or more precisely, to the right _____ _____.

right

1401. An afferent neural impulse from the left side of the body will eventually find its way to the _____ cerebral hemisphere.

cerebral hemisphere

right

1402. The right cerebral hemisphere receives nerve impulses from the left side of the body, whereas the left _____ _____ receives neural impulses from the _____ side of the body.

right

right; left

1403. Because we shall use this information later, it is important that you remember that nerve impulses from the left side of the body run to the _____ cerebral hemisphere, whereas nerve impulses from the _____ side of the body run to the _____ cerebral hemisphere.

nervous system

1404. An afferent nerve impulse may cross to the opposite side of the spinal cord at the point at which it enters the spinal cord, or it may cross higher up in the central _____ _____.

opposite/other

1405. In some cases, afferent neural impulses go immediately to the OPPOSITE side of the spinal cord. But in other cases, they run up the spinal cord on the side at which they entered and cross over to the _____ side later.

spinal cord

1406. Regardless of where afferent neural impulses enter, they all cross over to the opposite side of the _____ _____ before they reach the cerebrum.

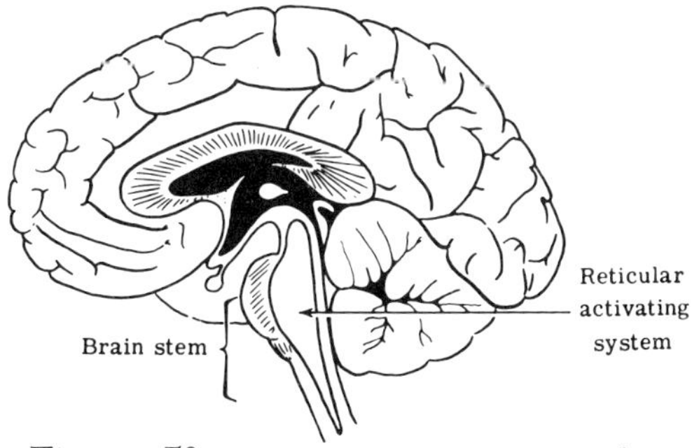

Reticular
activating
system

Brain stem

FIGURE 70

activating system

1407. In Figure 70, we see a representation of the RETICULAR ACTIVATING SYSTEM. The reticular _____ _____ is largely in the brain stem, but it also extends down into the spinal cord.

brain
stem

1408. We previously saw that neural impulses that ascend the spinal cord enter the brain at the _____ _____.

cranial

1409. Other afferent neural impulses are conducted directly to the brain stem by means of _____ nerves.

brain stem

1410. Regardless of whether a nerve impulse came from a cranial nerve or ascended the spinal cord, once it enters the _____ _____ it can go in one of two directions.

activating

1411. One direction that a nerve impulse can take is through the brain stem, bypassing the reticular _____ system. (Study the brain stem in Figure 70.)

activating system

1412. The second direction that an impulse can take, once it enters the brain stem, is to go through the reticular _____ _____.

reticular

1413. Nerve impulses that enter the brain stem may either go through the _____ activating system, or they may bypass this region.

activating system

1414. Because it activates the cerebral cortex, the important region located primarily in the brain stem is called the reticular _____ _____.

cortex

1415. When afferent neural impulses enter the reticular activating system, a large number of DIFFUSE (spread out in all directions) NEURAL IMPULSES then go to the cerebral _____.

neural impulses

1416. The reticular activating system activates the cerebral cortex by sending a number of diffuse _____ _____ to that structure.

reticular activating system

1417. The cerebral cortex is excited, or activated, by the numerous nerve impulses that come from the _____ _____.

cortex

impulses

1418. When the reticular activating system activates the cortex, the _____ is prepared for the receipt of additional neural _____.

activated

reticular activating system

1419. The cerebral cortex is excited, or _____, and thus prepared for the receipt of additional neural impulses, by means of diffuse impulses from the _____ _____.

reticular activating system

1420. Whereas the reticular activating system sends nerve impulses up to the cortex, the cortex also sends nerve impulses back down into the _____ _____.

cortex

reticular activating system

1421. When nerve impulses descend from the cerebral _____ to the reticular activating system, activation of the _____ _____ _____ occurs.

activate/excite/arouse

1422. We can thus see that there is a kind of "closed loop" between the reticular activating system and the cerebral cortex. That is, the reticular activating system sends neural impulses to activate, excite, or arouse the cerebral cortex, while the cerebral cortex also sends impulses to _____ the reticular activating system.

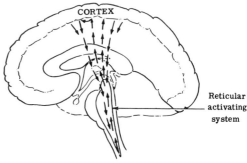

FIGURE 71

1423. In Figure 71, you can see a representation of this process. That is, afferent neural impulses that enter the reticular activating system are transmitted, in a diffuse pattern, up to the _____ _____.

cerebral cortex

1424. As a result of this bombardment of the cortex by incoming impulses from the reticular activating system, the cortex is aroused, or _____.

activated/excited

1425. The cortex, in turn, sends nerve impulses back down into the reticular activating system, whereupon this region also is excited, or _____.

activated/aroused

1426. It is possible to artificially stimulate various parts of the brain by a number of means. For example, small amounts of electricity can be sent into tiny electrodes that are inserted in the cerebral cortex. By electrically stimulating the cerebral cortex (this is not painful), it has been observed that the reticular activating system is excited, or _____.

activated/aroused

1427. When a part of the brain, such as the cortex, is activated, there is an increase in the number of _____ _____ that flow along its neurons.

nerve impulses

1428. Similarly, by electrically stimulating the reticular activating system, an increase in activity of the _____ _____ can be demonstrated.

cerebral cortex

1429. Such experimental findings as these justify our conclusion that there is a "closed loop" between the

reticular activating system; cerebral cortex

_____   _____

_____ and the _____ _____.

1430. The name "reticular ACTIVATING system" is appropriate because it has been demonstrated, in a number of ways, that this system _____ the cerebral cortex.

activates

1431. To consider another example, it was found that if the reticular activating system of a sleeping cat was electrically stimulated, the cat would stop sleeping and awaken, or _____ up.

wake

1432. Another finding was that a normally awake cat would become extremely alert when his reticular activating system was electrically _____.

stimulated

1433. In another experiment, it was found that if the reticular activating system was isolated by cutting it off from the cerebral cortex, the cat would no longer stay awake, but would go to _____ for a long period of time.

sleep

1434. It thus seems clear that the reticular activating system is important for the SLEEPING and WAKING states. If the reticular activating system is not active, then the individual seems to be in a _____ state.

sleeping

1435. But when the reticular activating system is active, the individual seems to be in a _____ state.

waking

1436. At night, when a person is sleeping, his reticular activating system is _____ active.

not/less

1437. During the day, when a person is in his normal waking state, however, the reticular activating system is _____.

active

afferent
neural impulses

1438. When a person is asleep, very few external stimuli are exciting his receptors. Hence, during the sleeping state, relatively few _____ _____ _____ are being conducted into the reticular activating system.

reticular activating
system

1439. Because very few neural impulses are entering the reticular activating system during sleep, the _____ _____ _____ tends to "shut down."

cerebral cortex

1440. And when the reticular activating system is not active, the _____ _____ is not very active.

sleeping

1441. There is a reduced amount of activity in the cerebral cortex and in the reticular activating system, when a person is in the _____ state.

receptors

1442. When he is awake, however, numerous stimuli impinge on his _____ to set off numerous afferent neural impulses.

waking

1443. Consequently, a large number of afferent neural impulses are entering the reticular activating system during the _____ state.

medulla; pons
(either order)

1444. The brain stem is important, not only because it contains the reticular activating system, but because it also contains certain vital nervous centers. We recall that the brain stem has two major structures: 1) the _____, and 2) the _____.

center

1445. The medulla, for instance, has a nervous CENTER that controls BREATHING. Another nervous _____ in the medulla controls the beating of the HEART.

breathing
heart

1446. Two important nervous centers in the medulla control _____ and the beating of the _____.

breathe

1447. If you EXTIRPATED (cut out) the nervous center that controls breathing, the person would not be able to _____ properly.

extirpate

1448. Similarly, if one were to cut out, or _____ the nervous center that controlled heart rate, the person's heart would not beat properly.

extirpate

1449. When we perform an operation that destroys, cuts out, or burns out a section of nervous tissue, we say that we _____ that tissue.

extirpate

1450. In order to better understand how the brain functions, physiologists and physiological psychologists frequently perform operations on lower animals. In performing these operations, they frequently destroy, or _____, a certain part of the brain.

brain

1451. It is then possible to observe how the animal behaves with that section of his _____ missing, or extirpated.

extirpated

1452. By thus comparing an animal's behavior before and after a given part of the brain has been _____, knowledge about the function of that part can be obtained.

center

1453. There are intricate neural pathways between the heart and the nervous _____ in the medulla that controls heart rate.

medulla

1454. Hence, nerve impulses are constantly going between the heart and the nervous center in the _____ that controls heart rate.

nerve impulses

1455. You can thus see that the extirpation of a center, such as those for heart rate or breathing, will interrupt the normal flow of _____ _____ that regulate such bodily activities.

center

1456. It was by the tedious process of extirpating small sections of the medulla that scientists discovered the existence of the nervous _____ that controls heart rate.

kinesthetic

1457. Another important function of the brain stem is to receive nerve impulses from the kinesthetic receptors in muscles. Recall that when a muscle contracts, it stimulates the _____ receptors embedded in it.

muscle

1458. The kinesthetic receptors embedded in muscles are called _____ spindles.

spindles

brain

1459. When muscle _____ in the muscles are activated, they send nerve impulses up the spinal cord to the _____ stem.

stem

muscles

1460. The brain _____, in turn, sends nerve impulses back down the spinal cord to the effectors, or, more specifically, to the _____.

muscles; brain stem

1461. In the functioning of the KINESTHETIC sense, nerve impulses are conducted to the brain stem, and the brain stem sends impulses back to the muscles. In this way, a continual exchange of nerve impulses occurs between the _____ and the _____ _____.

kinesthetic

1462. We previously saw that integrated behavior is made possible by the _____ sense.

integrated

1463. It is the rapid and frequent interchange between the muscles and the brain stem that contributes to some of our well-coordinated, _____ behavior, such as walking.

neural
impulses; stem

1464. When we take a step, the contraction of muscles in our legs sends afferent _____ _____ to the brain _____.

efferent

1465. Immediately, on receipt of these afferent neural impulses, the brain stem sends _____ neural impulses back down to the muscles causing them to contract again so that the next step may be taken.

brain
stem

1466. We have seen that all afferent neural impulses, which ascend the spinal cord, enter the _____ _____.

muscles

1467. From the brain stem, the impulses frequently go back down the spinal cord to cause the contraction of _____.

cranial

1468. We previously saw that the majority of afferent neural impulses enter the brain stem regardless of whether they ascend the spinal cord or are conducted directly into this part of the brain by _____ nerves.

reticular

1469. On entering the brain stem, nerve impulses may go in either of two directions. For one, they may enter the _____ activating system.

brain
stem

1470. Or they may bypass the reticular activating system and go through other parts of the _____ _____.

stem

1471. Recall that the internal structure of the brain called the thalamus, is located directly above the brain _____.

brain stem

1472. Nerve impulses that bypass the reticular activating system go directly to the thalamus when they leave the _____ _____.

cortex

1473. We also saw that nerve impulses that leave the reticular activating system eventually end up in the cerebral _____.

nerve
impulses

1474. While on their way from the reticular activating system to the cortex, these _____ _____ go through the thalamus.

thalamus

1475. Therefore, we can say that all nerve impulses that leave the brain stem enter the internal structure of the brain called the _____.

thalamus

1476. Impulses that leave the brain stem go higher into the internal part of the brain called the _____.

thalamus

1477. When the thalamus receives nerve impulses from the brain stem, it directs those nerve impulses to various parts of the cortex. It can thus be seen that the _____ acts as a switching, or relay, station.

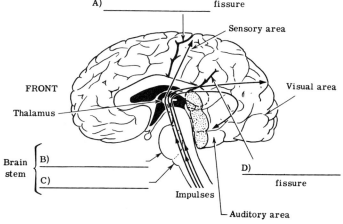

A) _____ fissure

Sensory area

FRONT

Visual area

Thalamus

Brain stem

B) _____

C) _____

Impulses

D) _____ fissure

Auditory area

FIGURE 72

A. *Central*
B. *Pons*
C. *Medulla*
D. *Lateral*

1478. Fill in the blanks in Figure 72.

cortex

1479. In Figure 72, we see how the thalamus directs nerve impulses to various parts of the cerebral _____.

center

1480. Like the brain stem, the thalamus contains several very specific nervous CENTERS. Neural impulses from the eye, for example, arrive at the nervous _____ in the thalamus for vision.

cortex

1481. When these visual nerve impulses arrive at the visual center of the thalamus, they are then directed to the visual area of the cerebral _____.

frontal

parietal

temporal

occipital

1482. Name the four lobes of each cerebral hemisphere. At the very front of the brain, one finds the _____ lobe; immediately behind the central fissure, one finds the _____ lobe; directly below the lateral fissure, one finds the _____ lobe; and at the very back of the brain, one finds the _____ lobe.

occipital

1483. In Figure 72, you can see that the visual area of the cortex is in the back part of the brain. Hence, you know that the visual area of the cortex lies in the _____ lobe.

cranial

1484. Nerve impulses from the eye are conducted into the brain along the _____ nerve called optic nerve.

optic

1485. When these visual nerve impulses leave the cranial nerve, called the _____ nerve, they eventually enter the thalamus.

thalamus

1486. More specifically, visual nerve impulses enter the visual center of the _____.

occipital

1487. From the thalamus, the impulses are then directed to the visual area of the cortex, which is located in the _____ lobe.

visual

1488. The occipital lobe contains the _____ area.

auditory

1489. Auditory nerve impulses from the ear are conducted into the brain stem along the cranial nerve called the _____ nerve.

thalamus

1490. The thalamus also contains an auditory center. From the brain stem, auditory nerve impulses enter the auditory center in the _____.

auditory center

1491. From the _____ _____ of the thalamus, these impulses are directed to the auditory area of the cortex.

lateral

1492. As can be seen in Figure 72, the auditory area of the cortex lies in the lobe below the _____ fissure.

temporal

1493. Hence, we may say that the auditory area of the cortex is in the _____ lobe.

auditory

1494. The temporal lobe contains the _____ area.

cortex

1495. The thalamus also contains a center that receives nerve impulses from all over the body. It then directs these nerve impulses to that part of the cerebral _____ called the SENSORY AREA.

central

1496. Note, in Figure 72, that the sensory area is immediately behind the _____ fissure.

sensory

1497. The area of the cortex directly behind the central fissure, and thus lying within the parietal lobe, is called the _____ area.

parietal

1498. Because the sensory area of the cortex lies immediately behind the central fissure, we know that the sensory area is in the _____ lobe.

kinesthetic

1499. We previously saw that the cutaneous and the kinesthetic receptors are widely distributed throughout the body. When the cutaneous and _____ receptors are stimulated, they send nerve impulses up the spinal cord and into the brain stem.

thalamus

1500. From the brain stem, these cutaneous and kinesthetic nerve impulses next go to a center in the _____.

sensory

1501. The thalamus then directs such impulses from the cutaneous and kinesthetic receptors to the part of the cortex called the _____ area.

central
cutaneous
kinesthetic
(either order)

1502. The sensory area of the cortex lies immediately behind the _____ fissure and receives nerve impulses from _____ receptors and from _____ receptors.

thalamus
sensory area

1503. Nerve impulses from cutaneous and kinesthetic receptors ascend the spinal cord, go through the brain stem, enter a particular center in the _____, and finally end up in the _____ _____ of the cortex.

cortex

thalamus

1504. We thus see that afferent neural impulses, whether they come from the eye, the ear, the cutaneous or the kinesthetic receptors, etc., are directed to specific areas of the cerebral _____ by the internal structure of the brain called the _____.

1505. Now let us summarize and extend what we have learned so far.

spinal
cord

1506. We have seen how afferent neural impulses typically enter the brain stem. If they come from spinal nerves, they ascend the _____ _____.

cranial

1507. Or they may come directly into the brain stem from _____ nerves.

1508. Once nerve impulses enter the brain stem, they either go into the reticular activating system, or they go through other parts of the brain stem, thus bypassing the _____ _____ system.

reticular activating

1509. When the impulses enter the reticular activating system, a number of diffuse impulses are then sent to activate the _____ _____.

cerebral cortex

1510. All nerve impulses that leave the brain stem, next go to the _____.

thalamus

1511. Regardless of whether or not nerve impulses leave the reticular activating system, or whether they leave other parts of the brain stem, they all next go to the _____.

thalamus

1512. The thalamus, then, acts like a switching station, in that it switches or directs the nerve impulses to specific areas of the cerebral _____.

cortex

1513. For example, nerve impulses that come from the ear are conducted along the auditory nerve into the brain stem and then into the auditory center of the internal structure of the brain called the _____.

thalamus

1514. The _____ center of the thalamus then directs these nerve impulses from the ear into the _____ area of the cerebral cortex.

auditory

auditory

1515. The temporal lobe of the cerebral cortex contains the _____ area.

auditory

1516. The auditory area of the cerebral cortex lies in the _____ lobe.

temporal

1517. We know that the cerebrum is divided into _____ cerebral hemispheres.

two

four

1518. We know too, that each cerebral hemisphere has _____ lobes.

occipital

1519. Thus, each cerebral hemisphere has a temporal lobe, a frontal lobe, a parietal lobe, and an _____ lobe.

auditory

1520. In general, the thalamus directs an incoming neural impulse to BOTH cerebral hemispheres. For instance, an impulse that enters the thalamus from the auditory nerve goes to the _____ area of the temporal lobe in the left cerebral hemisphere.

right

1521. It also goes to the auditory area of the temporal lobe in the _____ cerebral hemisphere.

temporal

1522. Auditory neural impulses go to both cerebral hemispheres. More particularly, they go to the auditory area located in the _____ lobe of both cerebral hemispheres.

optic

1523. When a nerve impulse comes from the eyes, along the cranial nerve called the _____ nerve, the thalamus directs that impulse to both cerebral hemispheres.

occipital

1524. More specifically, that visual impulse is directed to the visual area that lies in the _____ lobe of each cerebral hemisphere.

visual

1525. Each of the two occipital lobes receives visual nerve impulses in the area of the cortex called the _____ area.

optic
visual

1526. When a visual stimulus, such as a red light, excites the eyes, a nerve impulse is transmitted along the _____ nerve into the visual center of the thalamus and thence to the _____ areas of the cortex in both occipital lobes.

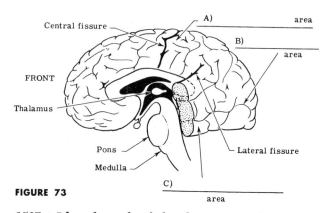

FIGURE 73

A. Sensory area
B. Visual area
C. Auditory area

1527. Identify each of the three areas of the cortex, shown in Figure 73, by filling in the blanks.

1528. Although we are not sure, it is widely believed that a person is "conscious" of a visual stimulus, such as a red light, when the resulting nerve impulse finds its way into the _____ area of the cortex.

visual

1529. Similarly, a person seems to be conscious of an auditory stimulus when the resulting impulse finds its way into the _____ _____ of the cortex contained in the _____ lobe.

auditory area
temporal

1530. The activation of neurons in the visual area, by incoming visual impulses, seems to make us conscious of external _____ stimuli.

visual

1531. What would happen if the visual area were electrically stimulated? When surgeons have stimulated the _____ _____, the individuals have reported visual experiences such as flashing lights or whirling colors.

visual area

1532. Similarly, when one of the two AUDITORY areas is electrically stimulated, the patient reports _____ experiences such as hearing humming or buzzing sounds.

auditory

1533. The sensory area of the cortex lies in the

parietal _____ lobe immediately behind the

central _____ fissure.

1534. When a small electrical stimulus is applied to the area behind the central fissure, called the

sensory _____ area, the patient reports various kinds of body "feelings," such as "My leg feels warm," or "I have a funny tingling sensation in my arm," or "I feel like my hand is moving" (even though it really is not moving).

1535. If the sensory area in a person's right cerebral hemisphere is stimulated, nerve impulses descend the spinal cord and cross over to the opposite side of the body. Thus, stimulation of the sensory area in the right cerebral hemisphere produces feelings in the

left _____ side of the body.

1536. We saw that ascending nerve impulses cross over the spinal cord to the OPPOSITE side. In like manner, descending neural impulses cross the spinal

opposite/other cord, at some level, to the _____ side of the body.

1537. Thus, stimulation of the left sensory area will

right produce feelings in the _____ side of the body.

1538. Nerve impulses that come from the left side of the body cross over to the opposite side of the spinal

right cord and go to the _____ cerebral hemisphere.

1539. Thus, if a person is stuck with a pin in his left arm, the resulting "conscious" sensation would occur when nerve impulses arrive in the part of the cortex,

sensory called the _____ area, of his right cerebral hemisphere.

1540. Nerve impulses that descend from the right cerebral hemisphere, cross over the spinal cord and

left go to the _____ side of the body.

1541. Thus, if a person's sensory area in the right cerebral hemisphere is stimulated, the resulting bodily
left sensation would be localized, or felt, in the ⸺⸺ side of his body.

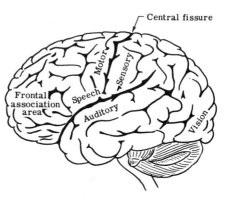

Central fissure

FIGURE 74

1542. In Figure 74, we see a diagram of the cortex of the left cerebral hemisphere. There we see that
temporal the auditory area is in the ⸺⸺⸺
parietal lobe, that the sensory area is in the ⸺⸺⸺ lobe, and that the occipital lobe contains the area for
vision ⸺⸺⸺.

1543. In Figure 74, we also see that the FRONTAL
frontal ASSOCIATION AREAS are located in the ⸺⸺⸺ lobes.

areas 1544. The frontal association ⸺⸺⸺ are especially well developed in man.

frontal 1545. What is the function of the ⸺⸺⸺ association areas?

1546. Unfortunately, we do not have a complete answer to this question. The little research that has been
association conducted on the frontal ⸺⸺⸺
areas ⸺⸺⸺ suggests that one function is related to attention.

1547. For example, when the frontal association areas of monkeys were extirpated, the monkeys could not maintain their attention to a task. Such results suggest that the frontal association areas function to

attention   help us maintain _____.

frontal   *1548.* One function of the _____ association areas seems to be to help us maintain

attention   _____.

attention   *1549.* Humans who have had their frontal association areas damaged seem to have difficulty in maintaining _____.

1550. Such people also appear to not worry about FUTURE events. Individuals who have accidentally had their frontal association areas damaged appear to

future   have lost much of their concern for _____ events.

1551. Poor ability to make plans about the future

frontal   seems to result from destruction of the _____

association areas   _____ _____.

1552. Making plans necessarily involves the anticipation of FUTURE events. Although the results of research are not clear, they suggest that the frontal association areas contribute to man's ability to antici-

future   pate _____ events.

1553. Although much more research needs to be conducted, what little information we have suggests that the frontal association areas are important for

attention   maintaining _____, and for anticipat-

future   ing _____ events.

1554. In Figure 74, you can note that the frontal lobe also contains a SPEECH AREA. The normal functioning

area   of the speech _____ is necessary in order for us to talk.

frontal   1555. The speech area is located in the _____ lobe.

speech   1556. People who have lesions in the part of the frontal lobe that contains the _____ area have SPEECH APHASIA (ə fā′zhə).

speech   1557. The loss of ability to speak a language is called _____ aphasia.

speech
aphasia   1558. If an otherwise normal person is unable to speak, we might suspect that he has _____ _____.

speak/talk   1559. A person who has speech aphasia is able to understand spoken language, but he himself is not able to _____.

speech area
cerebral   1560. Unlike the other areas of the cortex, the speech area does not appear in both cerebral hemispheres. Rather, the _____ _____ appears only in the left _____ hemisphere.

frontal; speech
aphasia   1561. If a person has a lesion in the portion of his _____ lobe called the _____ area, he will develop speech _____.

association areas
speech   1562. We can thus see that the frontal lobes are extremely important. They contain the frontal _____ _____ and the _____ area.

future
attention   1563. The frontal association areas seem to contribute to our ability to plan _____ events, and to maintain _____.

speak/talk   1564. The speech area is responsible for our ability to _____.

central

1565. In Figure 74, we see that the motor area lies directly in front of the _____ fissure.

motor area

front

1566. The sensory area is immediately in back of the central fissure, and the _____ _____ is immediately in _____ of the central fissure.

motor

1567. The neurons in the motor area extend down to neurons in the brain stem and the spinal cord that eventually connect to muscles. Nerve impulses from the _____ area thus find their way to muscles throughout the body.

motor

area

1568. If a particular place in a person's motor area is electrically stimulated, there results a contraction of muscles at a specific location in his body. For example, stimulation of a specific part of the _____ _____ might cause movement of the hand.

motor

movement

1569. Stimulation applied in another part of the motor area would cause MOVEMENT of the toes, whereas stimulation in still another part of the _____ area would cause _____ of the lips.

right

1570. Neurons from the left hemisphere cross over to the right side of the body as they descend the brain and spinal cord. Therefore, stimulation of the motor area in the left cerebral hemisphere produces movement in the _____ side of the body.

movement

left

1571. Stimulation of the motor area in the right cerebral hemisphere produces _____ in the _____ side of the body.

right

1572. If a person has a lesion in the motor area of the left cerebral hemisphere, a paralysis develops in the _____ side of his body.

cortex

1573. The motor area is a specific region in the cerebral _____ of both cerebral hemispheres.

motor area

1574. Whereas the speech area is located in the left cerebral hemisphere, the area directly in front of the central fissure, called the _____ _____, appears in both cerebral hemispheres.

central fissure

1575. The motor area is located directly in front of the _____ _____.

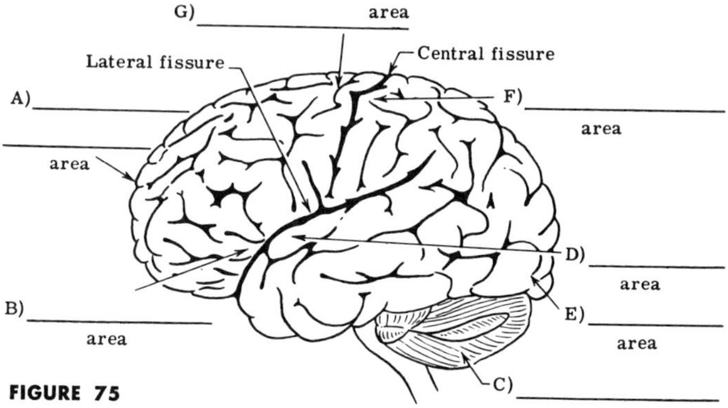

FIGURE 75

A. *Frontal associa-*
   tion area
B. *Speech area*
C. *Cerebellum*
D. *Auditory area*
E. *Visual (or*
   vision) area
F. *Sensory area*
G. *Motor area*

1576. Fill in the blanks to indicate the various parts of the brain.

brain

1577. A number of sections of the brain are concerned with the control of muscles. These sections of the _____ are connected together, either directly or indirectly, by means of groups of neurons.

muscles

1578. In studying the kinesthetic sense, we saw that nerve impulses go from muscles to the brain stem, and from the brain stem back to the _____.

motor

1579. We have also seen how the muscles on the right side of the body are controlled by the _____ area of the cerebral cortex, which is located in the left cerebral hemisphere.

motor   1580. In addition to the _____ area of the
brain   cortex and the _____ stem, the CEREBELLUM is
a third section of the brain that is intimately concerned with motor control.

1581. The sponge-like structure below the back of
cerebellum   the cerebrum, called the _____,
has widespread neural connections with the brain
stem and the motor area of the cortex.

1582. Three parts of the brain are intimately concerned with motor control of the muscles. These are
brain; motor   the _____ stem, the _____ area of the
cerebellum   cortex, and the _____.

1583. Not only do the nerve impulses, which come
from kinesthetic receptors, find their way to the brain
stem and to the cortex, they also go to the
cerebellum   _____.

1584. The cerebellum receives these impulses and
integrates them so that a series of smooth, coordinated
responses result. A lesion in the cerebellum would
result in a series of jerky RESPONSES, rather than in a
responses/   series of smooth, integrated _____.
movements

1585. Highly skilled and integrated responses de-
pend, in large part, on the cerebellum. The highly
developed movements of a bird in flight are possible
because a bird has a relatively large and well de-
cerebellum   veloped _____.

1586. The cerebellum works closely together with
various other portions of the brain concerned with
motor control. Among the areas of the brain con-
cerebellum   cerned with motor control are the _____;
brain; motor   the _____ stem, and the _____ area of
the cortex.

1587. As a result of the close cooperation of such portions of the brain, a person is able to make series of well coordinated, integrated _____.

responses/ movements/ behavior

1588. The brain is an exceedingly complex organ. Many of the FUNCTIONS of the brain have not been considered here, and, in fact, many of its functions are yet to be discovered. A consideration of two more _____ of the brain will conclude our present discussion of it.

functions

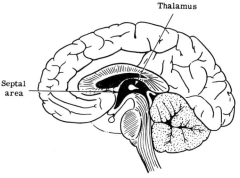

FIGURE 76

1589. In an interesting experiment, using white rats, tiny electrodes were inserted into an area of the brain called the septal area. As you can see in Figure 76, the septal _____ is close to the thalamus.

area

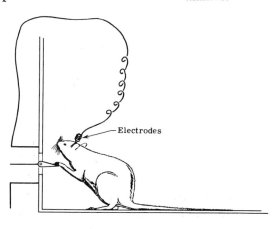

FIGURE 77

septal area

1590. In Figure 77, we see a diagram of the rat pressing the lever. Every time he pressed the lever a small amount of electricity would go through the wires into the electrode and into the internal part of his brain called the _____ _____.

electricity
septal

1591. The rat was then "free" to press the lever or not to press the lever. Every time he pressed the lever a small amount of _____ was delivered to his _____ area.

septal area

1592. The fascinating finding of this experiment was that the rat pressed the lever a large number of times. The conclusion was that shocking himself in the _____ _____ was a "pleasant" (rewarding) experience for the rat.

reward

1593. Because stimulation of the septal area seemed to provide a REWARD (a "pleasant experience"), that center has been called a _____ center.

septal area; reward

1594. The _____ _____ is a _____ center.

cortex

1595. The second interesting function that we will discuss concerns memory for past experiences. A surgeon, while performing a necessary operation, electrically stimulated several places in a patient's cerebral cortex. Stimulation of some of the places of the cerebral _____ produced a vivid MEMORY, or recall of past experiences.

stimulated

1596. For example, when a specific place in the cortex of the TEMPORAL LOBE was electrically _____, the patient said, "Yes, sir, I think I heard a mother calling her little boy somewhere. It seemed to be something that happened years ago."

memory

1597. Experiments such as these suggest that the brain stores memories of past events. In this example, stimulation of a particular part of the temporal lobe produced a vivid _____ of a past event.

temporal

1598. The results of this investigation indicated that a person can recall a past event when a special place in the _____ lobe of the cortex was stimulated.

1599. Let us now summarize the process by which a nerve impulse is conducted from a receptor to an effector.

dorsal

1600. When a receptor in the body sets off an afferent neural impulse, that impulse is conducted along a spinal nerve into a _____ root of the spinal cord.

ventral

brain
stem

1601. The impulse then may go in two directions: 1) out of the spinal cord through a _____ root to activate an effector; and 2) up the spinal cord into the lower part of the brain called the _____ _____ .

opposite, or other

1602. Afferent neural impulses always cross over the spinal cord and go to the cerebral hemisphere on the opposite side of the body. In like manner, impulses that descend from one cerebral hemisphere cross over to the _____ side of the body.

right

right

1603. Thus, afferent neural impulses from the left side of the body go to the _____ cerebral hemisphere, and nerve impulses that come from the left cerebral hemisphere control the _____ side of the body.

cranial

1604. If an afferent neural impulse is generated by a receptor in the head (e.g., the eyes), the impulse is transmitted along one of the _____ nerves, called the optic nerve, directly to the brain.

reticular activating

1605. When an afferent neural impulse enters the brain stem it may go in either of two directions: 1) into the _____ _____ system; or 2) it may bypass this region and go to other parts of the brain stem.

cortex

1606. Neural impulses that enter the reticular activating system produce a diffuse discharge of impulses that activates the cerebral _____.

activate/stimulate

1607. The cerebral cortex, in turn, sends impulses down to _____ the reticular activating system.

thalamus

1608. When an incoming neural impulse leaves the brain stem, it next enters one of several specific nervous centers in the internal part of the brain called the _____.

cortex

1609. The thalamus acts as a switching, or relay, station to direct these impulses to various areas of the cerebral _____.

auditory
brain

1610. For example, a nerve impulse from the ear runs along the cranial nerve, called the _____ nerve, directly into the _____ stem.

auditory

1611. The brain stem then sends the auditory impulse into the _____ center of the thalamus.

auditory
temporal

1612. From the auditory center of the thalamus, the impulse goes to the _____ area of the cortex that is located in the _____ lobe.

cerebral cortex

1613. Neural impulses relayed from the thalamus are directed to a large number of areas of the _____ _____.

visual

central; parietal

1614. For example, they may be directed to the area in the occipital lobe called the _____ area, or to the sensory area that is directly behind the _____ fissure in the _____ lobe.

central fissure

cerebellum

1615. Well integrated motor control involves making a series of coordinated responses. The integration of responses is controlled by various parts of the brain, such as the motor area, that lies directly in front of the _____ _____, by the brain stem, and by the rather large sponge-like structure below the occipital lobe called the _____.

left

1616. The speech area is a particularly important area in the frontal lobe of the _____ cerebral hemisphere.

ventral

1617. When nerve impulses descend from the brain, they leave the spinal cord by means of the _____ roots.

muscles; glands

1618. Impulses conducted out of the spinal cord by means of ventral roots, are transmitted along efferent nerves to one of the two types of effectors: _____ or _____.

THE NERVOUS SYSTEMS

Section XIV: The Peripheral Nervous System

central nervous system

1619. We have described the nature of the central nervous system. The brain and the spinal cord compose the _____ _____ _____.

system

1620. We have used the term "nervous systems" several times. We did this because there is more than one nervous _____ in the body.

brain; spinal cord

1621. The central nervous system is made up of the _____ and the _____ _____.

system

1622. All other nervous material compose the peripheral nervous _____.

central nervous

1623. That is, all nervous material outside of the _____ _____ system makes up the PERIPHERAL NERVOUS SYSTEM.

spinal cord

1624. To be more precise, we should say that the central nervous system includes all the nervous material within the cranium and the _____ _____.

central nervous system

1625. Because certain cranial nerves, such as the optic nerve, are encased entirely in the cranium, they belong to the _____ _____ _____.

1626. Other cranial nerves, however, extend outside of the cranium, to regions of the face, for example. Hence, some cranial nerves belong exclusively to the central nervous system while portions of other cranial nerves belong to the _____ nervous system.

peripheral

1627. In general, all nervous material that lies outside of the cranium and the _____ _____ belong to the _____ _____ system.

spinal cord
peripheral nervous

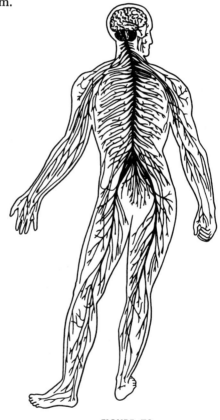

FIGURE 78

1628. In Figure 78, we see a representation of the nervous systems from a rear view. Note that all nerves throughout the body connect to the nervous material, in the central part of the body, that makes up the _____ _____ _____.

central nervous
system

peripheral

1629. In this simplified representation of the nervous systems you can get some idea that, like the central nervous system, the _____ nervous system is also very complex.

efferent

1630. The general function of the peripheral nervous system is to conduct afferent neural impulses into the central nervous system and to conduct _____ neural impulses out of the central nervous system.

spinal

1631. The nerves that enter the dorsal root and leave the ventral root of the spinal cord, are called _____ nerves.

cranial

1632. But the nerves that enter and leave the brain are called _____ nerves.

cranial; spinal

1633. The peripheral nervous system includes _____ and _____ nerves that lie outside of the central nervous system.

receptors

1634. As the cranial and spinal nerves move farther away from the central nervous system, they branch and divide into numerous smaller nerves. These smaller nerves receive neural impulses that are generated by _____ distributed throughout the body.

effectors

1635. In addition to transmitting nerve impulses from receptors to the central nervous system, these smaller nerves also deliver efferent neural impulses to _____ that are widely distributed throughout the body.

nervous system

1636. The peripheral nervous system has two divisions: 1) the AUTONOMIC (ô tə nŏm'ĭk) nervous system, and 2) the SOMATIC _____ _____.

peripheral

1637. Like the somatic nervous system, the autonomic nervous system is part of the larger _____ nervous system.

autonomic

1638. Note that it is called the autonomic and not the automatic nervous system: Write "autonomic," but do not write "automatic" _____.

efferent

1639. The autonomic nervous system is entirely ¡MOTOR in function. That is, it does NOT conduct afferent neural impulses into the central nervous system, but only conducts _____ neural impulses out of the central nervous system to effectors.

efferent

1640. The autonomic nervous system sends _____ neural impulses to various internal organs of the body, such as the heart, the glands, and blood vessels.

autonomic

1641. The contraction of the muscles in the stomach, which is necessary when we digest food, is an example of an internal organ that receives efferent neural impulses by means of the part of the peripheral nervous system called the _____ nervous system.

autonomic
nervous

1642. The intestines is another example of an internal ORGAN that is controlled by the _____ _____ system.

organs

1643. When a person is in an EMOTIONAL STATE, one thing that happens is that the various internal _____ of the body become "stirred up."

autonomic

1644. Changes in the action of the internal organs of the body during emotional states is due to increased activity of the _____ nervous system.

emotional

1645. The autonomic nervous system is especially active when a person is in an _____ state.

right

1646. Man has two ADRENAL glands, one located on the left side of the body, at about the waist line, and the second is located in the same place on the _____ side of the body.

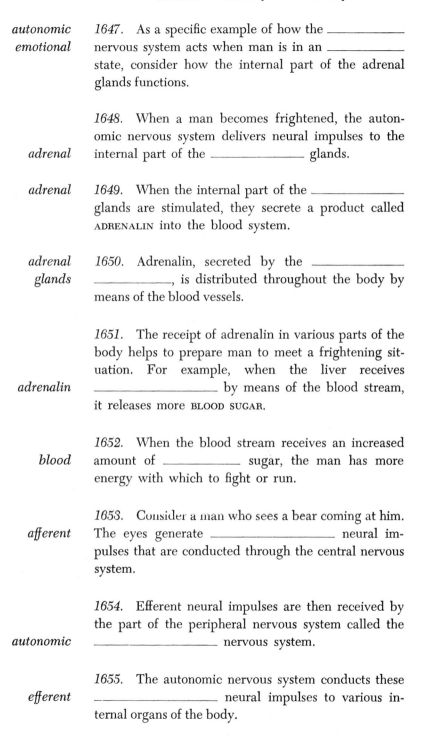

autonomic
emotional

1647. As a specific example of how the _____ nervous system acts when man is in an _____ state, consider how the internal part of the adrenal glands functions.

1648. When a man becomes frightened, the autonomic nervous system delivers neural impulses to the

adrenal

internal part of the _____ glands.

adrenal

1649. When the internal part of the _____ glands are stimulated, they secrete a product called ADRENALIN into the blood system.

adrenal
glands

1650. Adrenalin, secreted by the _____ _____, is distributed throughout the body by means of the blood vessels.

1651. The receipt of adrenalin in various parts of the body helps to prepare man to meet a frightening situation. For example, when the liver receives

adrenalin

_____ by means of the blood stream, it releases more BLOOD SUGAR.

blood

1652. When the blood stream receives an increased amount of _____ sugar, the man has more energy with which to fight or run.

afferent

1653. Consider a man who sees a bear coming at him. The eyes generate _____ neural impulses that are conducted through the central nervous system.

1654. Efferent neural impulses are then received by the part of the peripheral nervous system called the

autonomic

_____ nervous system.

efferent

1655. The autonomic nervous system conducts these _____ neural impulses to various internal organs of the body.

organs

1656. The increased activation of these internal _____ of the body helps the man to meet the emergency situation.

adrenal
adrenalin

1657. For example, efferent neural impulses are conducted to the internal part of the adrenal glands. This increased activity of the _____ glands produces an increase in the amount of _____ released into the blood stream.

sugar

1658. The adrenalin is then widely distributed so that various parts of the man's body are better prepared to meet the emergency situation. For example, the adrenalin activates the liver to release more blood _____, thus giving the man an increased amount of energy.

energy

1659. When an increased amount of blood sugar reaches the muscles of the arms and legs, the man has an increased amount of _____ with which to respond.

autonomic

1660. To consider another characteristic of the _____ nervous system, note that the internal organs of the body function in an AUTOMATIC fashion.

automatic

1661. It is the autonomic nervous system that allows these internal organs to function in an _____ fashion.

automatic

1662. For example, a person does not "decide" that his heart will beat, that he will sweat, or that he will digest his food. Rather, these internal functions are carried out in an _____ fashion by the autonomic nervous system.

medulla
autonomic
nervous

1663. Recall that we said there is a center in the MEDULLA that controls heart rate. The neural impulses from the heart rate center in the _____ are conducted to the heart by means of the _____ _____ system.

autonomic

automatic

1664. The integration of the heart rate center in the medulla, with the heart, by means of the _____ nervous system, allows the heart to beat continually in an _____ fashion.

peripheral

1665. To briefly summarize what we have said about the autonomic nervous system, recall that it is one of two divisions of the _____ nervous system.

from

organs

1666. The autonomic nervous system does NOT deliver neural impulses TO the central nervous system. Rather, it transmits impulses _____ the central nervous system to the internal _____ of the body.

automatic

1667. The autonomic nervous system controls the functioning of the internal organs of the body in an _____ fashion.

emotional

1668. It also is especially active when man is in an _____ state.

autonomic

1669. The peripheral nervous system may be divided into two parts: 1) the SOMATIC NERVOUS SYSTEM, and 2) the _____ nervous system.

somatic

1670. The autonomic nervous system serves the glands and internal organs of the body, whereas the _____ nervous system serves the receptors and the kinds of muscles required for walking, talking, writing, etc.

somatic

1671. The word "somatic" derives from the Greek *somatikos,* meaning "the body." The _____ nervous system is widely distributed throughout the body.

efferent

1672. The autonomic nervous system is efferent in nature only, but the somatic nervous system is BOTH afferent and _____ in nature.

1673. That is, nerve impulses generated by receptors are conducted to the central nervous system by means of spinal, and portions of cranial, nerves that are part

somatic nervous   of the _____ _____ system.

1674. Similarly, nerve impulses conducted out of the central nervous system are transmitted to muscles used in such activities as running or shaking hands,

spinal   by means of the cranial or _____ nerves that

somatic   are part of the _____ nervous system.

1675. Whereas the autonomic nervous system func-

automatic   tions in an _____ fashion, the somatic nervous system functions in a more "voluntary" fashion.

1676. For example, one does not decide that he is

decide   going to secrete adrenalin, but one could _____ that he will raise his right hand.

1677. A so-called "voluntary" act, such as raising your right hand, results from the transmission of neural impulses from the central nervous system to muscles in the right arm. When these impulses are received in

muscles   the right arm, _____ contract and the right arm is raised.

1678. By the term "voluntary" act, or response, we mean that the person can talk about the response before he performs it. That is, he can say to himself or to others that he has just "decided" to raise his right hand. When a person can say that he is going to perform a response before he actually performs it, we can

voluntary   say that the response is a _____ response.

1679. If a person can tell us that he is going to make a response, then we may call that response a

voluntary   _____ response.

voluntary

1680.   On the other hand, if the person cannot talk about the response (either to himself or to others) before he makes it, we would not refer to that response as a _____ response.

automatic

1681.   When a person cannot talk about a response before he makes it, we say that the response is automatic, rather than voluntary. The only difference between the physiology of voluntary and _____ responses is that the voluntary response is more complex.

automatic

1682.   Voluntary responses are of the same nature as _____ responses, but they are physiologically more complex.

automatic

1683.   The important point is that when we talk about voluntary responses we do not mean to suggest that they are caused by "mental energy," or by the "will." Thus, voluntary responses are merely more complex than _____ responses—both types are produced by nerve impulses.

afferent

efferent

1684.   The somatic nervous system delivers _____ neural impulses from receptors to the central nervous system and _____ neural impulses from the central nervous system to muscles.

effectors

1685.   To better understand the nature of the effectors activated by the autonomic nervous system and by the somatic nervous system, let us now study these _____ that are distributed throughout the body.

EFFECTORS

Section XV: Muscles

effectors   1686.   Efferent neural impulses may activate one of the two major types of _____: muscles or glands.

muscle; gland   1687.   When an efferent neural impulse activates an effector, be it a _____ or _____, we say that a RESPONSE results.

response   1688.   For example, when a muscle contracts, we say that the organism has made a _____.

gland   1689.   A response is also made when a _____ secretes its product.

1690.   In a way, a nerve is similar to a muscle. That is, a nerve is a bundle or collection of tiny nerve fibers, and a MUSCLE is a bundle or collection of tiny

muscle   _____ fibers.

Muscle

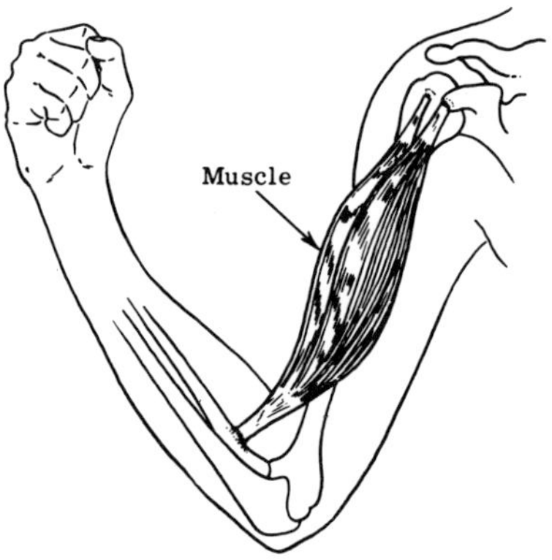

FIGURE 79

muscle

1691. In Figure 79, we see a number of muscle fibers that are collected, or bound together to form a _____.

A muscle fiber

FIGURE 80

muscle

1692. In Figure 80, we see a diagram of one kind of _____ fiber.

muscle

1693. When a nerve impulse arrives at a muscle, it causes a number of muscle fibers to contract. This is because a single efferent nerve fiber joins several _____ fibers.

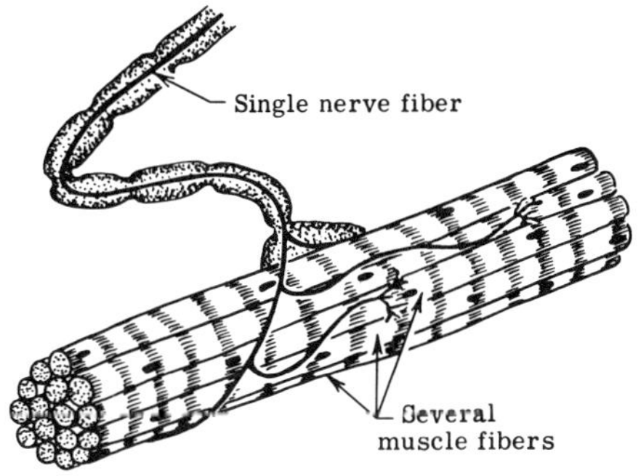

Single nerve fiber

Several muscle fibers

FIGURE 81

muscle fibers

1694. In Figure 81, we see an example of how a single nerve fiber makes junction with several _____ _____.

muscle
fibers

1695. Thus, an efferent neural impulse that runs along a single neuron, causes a number of _____ _____ to contract.

efferent

1696. Let us now see just what happens when a muscle fiber receives an _____ neural impulse.

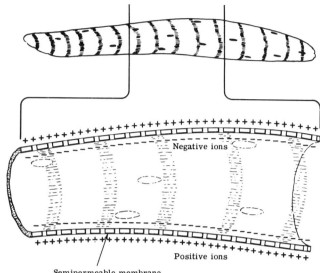

FIGURE 82

membrane

1697.   In the top of Figure 82, we see a diagram of a single muscle fiber. Just like the neuron, the muscle fiber is encased in a semi-permeable _____.

semi-permeable
membrane

1698.   In the lower part of Figure 82, we see an enlarged diagram of a portion of a muscle fiber. Like the resting neuron, the resting muscle fiber has positive ions on the outside of the _____ _____.

outside
inside

1699.   In Figure 82, we see that in the normal resting state the muscle fiber has positive ions on the _____ of its semi-permeable membrane and negative ions on the _____ of its semi-permeable membrane.

positive
negative

1700.   When a nerve impulse arrives at a muscle fiber, this "balance" between _____ ions on the outside and _____ ions on the inside is disturbed.

inside

1701.   The disturbance of the balance causes the positive ions to move through tiny holes to the _____ of the semi-permeable membrane.

efferent

1702. When this balance between positive and negative ions is disturbed by the arrival of an _____ neural impulse, the muscle fiber contracts.

contract

1703. Because each efferent nerve fiber connects to SEVERAL muscle fibers, the arrival of a single efferent neural impulse causes several muscle fibers to _____.

outside

negative

1704. The arrival of an efferent neural impulse at a group of muscle fibers causes the positive ions on the _____ of the semi-permeable membrane of each muscle fiber to move to the inside where they come in contact with _____ ions.

contract

1705. When this balance between positive and negative ions is disturbed, each muscle fiber connected to the efferent neuron starts to _____.

efferent

1706. Each muscle contains a large number of muscle fibers. Furthermore, a number of _____ neurons connect with each muscle.

contract

1707. When a number of nerve impulses arrives at a muscle along the various efferent nerve fibers, they cause a large number of muscle fibers to _____.

efferent

1708. Thus, the whole muscle contracts when all of its muscle fibers are caused to contract by the arrival of a number of _____ neural impulses.

electricity

1709. Just as in the case of the neuron, the flow of positive ions to the inside of the semi-permeable membrane generates "electricity." Hence, when a muscle fiber contracts, a certain amount of _____ is generated.

1710. When a neuron fires, we can measure the amount of electricity that flows through it. In like manner, when a muscle fiber fires, or more precisely, when it _____, there is a measurable amount of electricity generated.

contracts

1711. When a nerve impulse arrives at a muscle fiber, the balance between positive and _____ ions is disturbed.

negative

1712. At this time, the positive ions move to the inside of the semi-permeable membrane, and _____ is generated as the muscle fiber _____.

electricity
contracts

1713. The All or None Law applies to the muscle fiber, as well as to the neuron. Thus, if a muscle fiber contracts, it will give off _____ its energy.

all

1714. If the muscle fiber fails to contract, _____ of its energy is given off.

none

1715. The All or None Law applies to both neurons and _____ fibers.

muscle

1716. During contraction, the positive ions move to the _____ of the semi-permeable membrane.

inside

1717. As soon as a muscle fiber contracts, all its energy is expended and the recovery phase is started. The recovery _____ starts immediately after contraction.

phase

1718. It is during the recovery phase that the positive ions start to return to their original position _____ the semi-permeable membrane.

outside

1719. Positive ions move to the inside of the semi-permeable membrane when the muscle fiber _____, and they return to the outside during the _____ _____.

contracts
recovery phase

contract

1720. Once all of the positive ions have returned to the outside of the semi-permeable membrane, the muscle fiber is recharged and is again ready to "fire" or _____.

muscle

1721. Whereas all the muscle fibers in the body function in the general manner described above, there are three different types of _____ fibers.

muscle fiber

1722. The first type of _____ _____ is that used in such activities as talking, running, and shaking hands.

skeletal

1723. This first type of muscle fiber is called SKELETAL muscle. Because it is attached to the bones, or skeleton, of the body, the first type of muscle fiber is called _____ muscle.

skeletal
muscle

1724. The type of muscle that we feel just beneath our skin is used in activities such as walking or moving our hands. This muscle is attached to the bones of the body, and is called _____ _____.

Striations

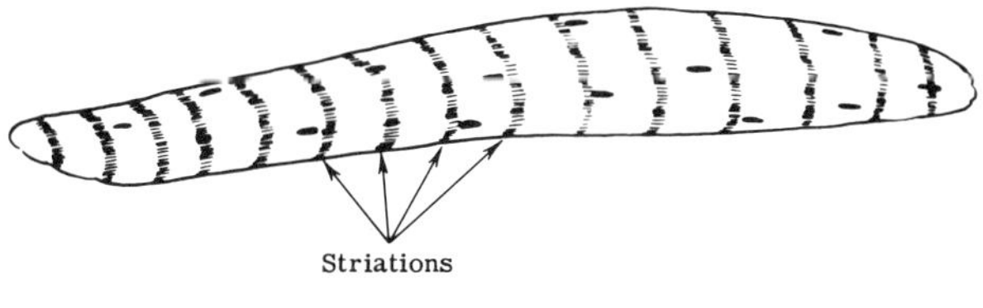

FIGURE 83

striated
skeletal

1725. In Figure 83, we can note the small stripes, or striations (threadlike lines), in a skeletal muscle fiber. Because skeletal muscle is STRIATED (strī'āt əd) sometimes it is called _____ muscle as well as _____ muscle.

striated
muscle

1726. Another name for skeletal muscle is _____ _____.

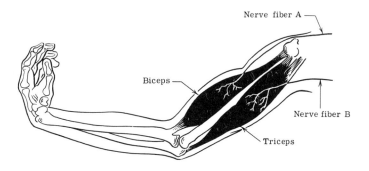

Nerve fiber A

Biceps

Nerve fiber B

Triceps

FIGURE 84

muscle

1727. In Figure 84, we see the well-known biceps (bī'sĕps) and triceps (trī'sĕps) muscles of the upper arm. Note that nerve fiber A connects to the biceps _____.

contract

1728. If nerve impulses run along nerve fiber A, they will cause the biceps muscle to _____.

contracts

1729. When the biceps muscle _____, it pulls on the bone of the lower arm.

biceps

1730. When the bone of the lower arm is pulled on by the _____ muscle, the lower arm moves up.

arm

1731. The contraction of the biceps muscle pulls on the bone of the lower arm, thus causing the lower _____ to bend up at the elbow.

contraction; biceps

1732. Bending of the arm at the elbow is caused by the _____ of the _____ muscle.

contracts

1733. Now suppose that nerve impulses arrive at the triceps muscle, along nerve fiber B. In this case the triceps muscle _____.

contracts

1734. When the triceps muscle _____, it pulls on the lower bone in the forearm, thus causing the arm to straighten out again.

contraction

1735. Bending the arm up is caused by the _____ of the biceps muscle, whereas straightening the arm is caused by the contraction of the _____ muscle.

triceps

skeletal/striated

1736. The biceps and triceps muscles are good examples of the type of muscle that we call _____ muscle.

Biceps

Triceps

Pectoralis major

External oblique

Sheath of rectus abdominis

Sartorius
Gracilis
Quadriceps femoris

Gastrocnemius

skeletal/striated

1737. In Figure 85, we see a diagram of a number of skeletal muscles of the body. It is not necessary that you learn the names of all these muscles, but you can get a general idea of how the type of muscle, which we call _____ muscle, is distributed throughout the body.

skeletal/striated

1738. By the systematic contraction of _____ muscles throughout the body, we perform such activities as sitting, running, and talking.

system

1739. Recall that the somatic nervous _____ controls the type of muscle used in such activities as walking, running, talking, etc.

skeletal muscles

1740. We now know that muscles used for such activities are called _____ _____.

somatic
nervous; skeletal

1741. Hence, we may say that the _____ _____ system controls the _____ muscles of the body.

somatic

1742. The so-called "voluntary" responses, such as "deciding" to raise your right hand above your head, are controlled by the _____ nervous system.

contract

1743. The somatic nervous system controls voluntary responses by causing the appropriate skeletal muscles to _____.

voluntary

1744. Because skeletal, or striated muscles are used in making VOLUNTARY responses, they are also sometimes called _____ muscles.

skeleton/bones

1745. Skeletal muscles are known by three different names. They are called skeletal muscles because they are attached to the _____ of the body.

striated

1746. Because they are striated, skeletal muscles are also known as _____ muscles.

voluntary

1747. The third name for skeletal muscles is due to their use in voluntary activities. Hence, they are also called _____ muscles.

somatic
skeletal; striated
voluntary
(any order)

1748. The three names for the type of muscle controlled by the _____ nervous system are: 1) _____ muscles, 2) _____ muscles, and 3) _____ muscles.

muscle

1749. The first type of muscle is skeletal muscle, whereas the second type is smooth _____.

striated

1750. We saw that because it is striated, skeletal muscle is also called _____ muscle.

not

1751.   A major distinguishing feature between skeletal muscle and smooth muscle is that skeletal muscle is striated, but smooth muscle is _____ striated.

smooth

1752.   Because it lacks striations, and is thus SMOOTH in appearance, the second type of muscle is called _____ muscle.

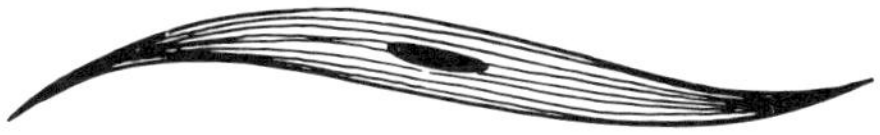

FIGURE 86

smooth
muscle

1753.   In Figure 86, we see a diagram of a _____ _____ fiber.

striations/stripes

1754.   Note that the smooth muscle fiber does not have _____.

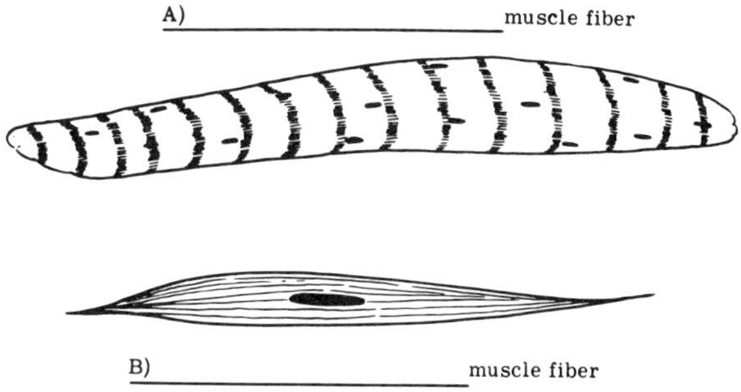

A) _____ muscle fiber

B) _____ muscle fiber

FIGURE 87

A. skeletal
B. smooth

1755.   In Figure 87, we see the first two types of muscle. Label the type of each fiber in the blanks provided.

skeletal
smooth

1756.   In Figure 87, you can see the _____ muscle fiber is larger than the _____ muscle fiber.

striations; smooth
smooth
skeletal

1757.   Two ways to distinguish between skeletal and smooth muscle fibers are: 1) skeletal muscle fibers contain _____, whereas _____ muscle fibers do not; and 2) that _____ muscle fibers are smaller than _____ muscle fibers.

smooth

1758. The first two distinctions between skeletal and _____ muscle fibers concerns their structure.

function

1759. The third distinction concerns how they FUNC-TION. Smooth and skeletal muscle fibers _____ somewhat differently when they contract.

smooth
muscle

1760. For example, when a skeletal muscle fiber receives a nerve impulse, it contracts almost immediately. This is not the case with a _____ _____ fiber.

smooth
skeletal

1761. That is, it takes a longer time for _____ muscle to contract than it does for _____ muscle.

function

1762. The first two distinctions between skeletal and smooth muscle concerned their structure. The third distinction concerns how they _____ when they contract.

smooth
skeletal

1763. One way in which they function differently is that _____ muscle contracts more slowly than does _____ muscle.

slowly

1764. Smooth muscle contracts more _____ than does skeletal muscle.

faster

1765. To put it the other way, skeletal muscle contracts more rapidly, or _____, than does smooth muscle.

smooth

1766. Another distinction between smooth and skeletal muscle concerns their location in the body. Skeletal muscle is distributed just beneath the skin, on the outside parts of the body, whereas _____ muscle tends to be more in the internal part of the body.

skeletal

1767. Muscles in the arms and legs are made up of _____ muscle.

smooth

1768. A number of internal organs of the body, however, contain _____ muscle.

internal

1769. The stomach and intestines are examples of _____ organs of the body.

smooth

1770. Internal organs of the body, such as the stomach and intestines, contain _____ muscle.

internal; smooth

1771. The bladder is another example of an _____ organ that contains _____ muscle.

rapid/fast

1772. Because skeletal muscle contracts rapidly, movements or responses involving skeletal muscles are, themselves, rather _____.

rapid/fast

1773. The contraction of skeletal muscles produces _____ responses.

smooth

1774. In contrast to skeletal muscle, however, _____ muscle contracts rather slowly.

slow

1775. Thus, the contraction of smooth muscle results in rather _____ responses.

fast/rapid
slow

1776. Skeletal muscle produces _____ responses, while smooth muscle produces _____ responses.

slow

1777. For example, the movement of the arm can be quite fast, but responses of the stomach or intestines are rather _____.

quick/fast

1778. A person may have to be very quick in jumping out of the way of a car, but he need not be so _____ in digesting his food.

skeletal

1779. To get out of the way of a car, a person relies on the rapid, or fast, contraction of his _____ muscles.

smooth

1780. However, in the more leisurely activity of digesting food, the relatively slow contraction of the _____ muscles in the stomach suffices.

smooth

1781. In addition to the internal organs, _____ muscle may be found in the blood vessels that are so widely distributed throughout the body.

blood

contracts

1782. When the smooth muscle, contained in the _____ vessels, receives nerve impulses, that muscle _____.

blood

1783. The contraction of the smooth muscles in the blood vessel helps direct the flow of _____ along its course.

blood

1784. Hence, an additional function of smooth muscle is to help distribute _____ throughout the body.

blood

1785. A continual supply of fresh blood is needed in various regions of the body. This supply is furnished by the automatic functioning of the _____ vessels.

smooth

1786. The AUTOMATIC contraction of the _____ muscle, contained in the blood vessels, helps to distribute a fresh supply of blood throughout the body.

automatic

1787. A person does not have to "decide" that he will contract the smooth muscles in his blood vessels. It is for this reason we say that the contraction of smooth muscles in the blood vessels is _____.

automatic

1788. The distribution of blood, throughout the body, occurs in an automatic fashion. Various internal organs of the body also function in an _____ fashion.

automatic

1789. The stomach is an example of an internal organ that functions in an _____ fashion.

smooth

1790. That is, we do not have to decide to contract the _____ muscles of the stomach in order to digest food.

automatic

1791. Similarly, the contraction of the smooth muscles in the intestines is not a voluntary response, but is, rather, an _____ response.

autonomic

1792. Recall that the peripheral nervous system has two divisions: 1) the somatic nervous system, and 2) the _____ nervous system.

somatic

1793. We previously saw that skeletal muscle is controlled by the _____ nervous system.

skeletal

1794. We also saw that a voluntary response, such as raising the hand over the head, results from the contraction of _____ muscle.

skeletal
voluntary

1795. That is, the somatic nervous system causes _____ muscles to contract, thus producing such _____ responses as raising the hand over the head.

smooth

1796. The somatic nervous system controls skeletal muscle whereas the autonomic nervous system controls _____ muscle.

autonomic

1797. The smooth muscle of the body is controlled by the _____ nervous system.

smooth

1798. We previously learned that the autonomic nervous system functions automatically; we now know that it controls the _____ muscles of the body.

smooth

1799. The arms and legs contain skeletal muscles, but the internal organs of the body contain _____ muscle.

autonomic

1800. The internal organs contain smooth muscle which is controlled by the _____ nervous system.

1801. Because the autonomic nervous system functions automatically and because it controls the internal organs of the body, we can now better understand how the internal organs function in an _____ fashion.

automatic

1802. That is, nerve impulses are delivered automatically to the internal organs of the body by the _____ _____ system.

autonomic nervous

1803. The autonomic nervous system controls the internal organs by causing the smooth muscle, contained in them, to _____.

contract

1804. Instead of exercising voluntary control over our internal organs, they function in an _____ fashion.

automatic

1805. Responses, such as talking or running, result from the transmission of neural impulses along the somatic nervous system to _____ muscles.

skeletal

1806. However, responses, such as digesting food, occur because the _____ nervous system delivers neural impulses to _____ muscle.

autonomic
smooth

1807. We are constantly making a large number of automatic responses. Activities like breathing, digesting food, and the flow of blood are examples of such _____ responses.

automatic

1808. We have now considered two of the three types of muscle fibers found in the body. These are _____ and _____ muscle fibers.

smooth; skeletal
(either order)

1809. The third and last type is called CARDIAC (kär′-dĭ ăk) muscle. _____ muscle is found in the heart.

Cardiac

1810. The word CARDIAC refers to the heart. It is for this reason that we call the muscle found in the heart

cardiac muscle _____   _____ .

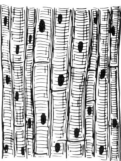

Cardiac muscle tissue

FIGURE 88

1811. In Figure 88, we see a diagram of some

cardiac _____ muscle tissue.

1812. You can see that cardiac muscle looks different

skeletal; smooth from either _____ or _____
(either order) muscle.

1813. The fibers of cardiac muscle found in the

heart _____ are intimately interwoven.

1814. That is, these fibers form an irregular mesh-work—there are numerous complex, and intimate con-

cardiac nections among the _____ muscle fibers of the heart.

1815. The heart is actually a hollow muscle made up

cardiac of finely interwoven _____ muscle fibers.

1816. Being hollow, the cardiac muscle that com-

heart poses the _____ contains blood.

1817. Cardiac muscle forms a hollow heart and con-

blood tains _____ .

1818. Like skeletal and smooth muscle, when cardiac

contracts muscle receives a nerve impulse, it _____ .

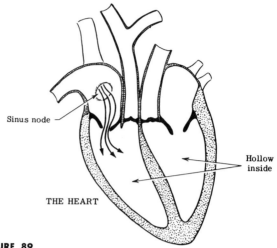

THE HEART

FIGURE 89

heart

1819. In Figure 89, we see a diagram of a human _____. Note the SINUS (sī′nəs) NODE.

node

1820. Nerve impulses are delivered to the heart at the sinus _____.

sinus node

1821. Nerve impulses, which arrive at the part of the heart called the _____ _____, regulate contractions of the cardiac muscle region.

cardiac

heart

1822. Recall that the _____ muscle fibers of the _____ are intimately connected in an irregular meshwork.

contractions

1823. Thus, when CONTRACTIONS start at the sinus node, those _____ spread to other fibers throughout the heart.

heart

1824. That is, an initial contraction at the sinus node gradually spreads to the intimately inter-connected muscle fibers in the rest of the _____.

sinus node

1825. The hollow muscle that makes up the heart starts to contract at the _____ _____, and these contractions spread throughout the rest of the heart.

blood

1826. When the muscle fibers of the heart contract, pressure is produced on the _____ that is inside it.

heart

1827. The increased pressure on the blood inside the heart, forces the blood out of the _____ and into the blood vessels.

blood

1828. Once blood is forced out of the heart, it is carried along the _____ vessels by the systematic contraction of the smooth muscle contained in those vessels.

heart

1829. Recall that there is a center in the medulla controlling heart rate. This center automatically sends nerve impulses to the part of the _____ called the sinus node.

medulla; sinus node

1830. These impulses come regularly from the center in the _____ to the _____ _____ of the heart.

regular

1831. These impulses function to REGULATE the heart rate. That is, their REGULAR arrival at the sinus node causes the heart to beat in a _____, rather than random, fashion.

cardiac

1832. Contractions that start at the sinus node spread throughout the numerous, intertwined _____ muscle fibers of the heart.

pressure

1833. The contraction of the entire heart produces _____ on the blood contained inside.

vessels/stream

1834. The increase in pressure then forces the blood out of the heart and into the blood _____ of the body.

EFFECTORS

Section XVI: The Glands

muscles; glands

1835. We know that there are two general types of effectors: _____ and _____.

skeletal; smooth
cardiac
(any order)

1836. We have now considered the three types of muscles: _____, _____, and _____ muscles.

glands

1837. It now remains for us to consider the second general type of effector, namely, the _____.

automatically

1838. We have seen how the smooth and cardiac muscles work automatically. Like these types of muscles, the glands also function _____.

secrete

1839. By this, we mean we do not have to "decide" that a certain gland will secrete its product. Rather, glands _____ their product without our "deciding" that they should.

sweat

1840. For example, we know that sweat glands secrete _____ automatically.

adrenalin

1841. We also know that the internal portion of the adrenal gland automatically secretes the product called _____.

automatically

1842. There are two types of glands in the body, and both types function _____.

two   1843. When either of these _____ types of glands secrete their product, we say that a response results.

1844. The first type of gland is called a duct gland, whereas the second type is called a ductless

gland   _____.

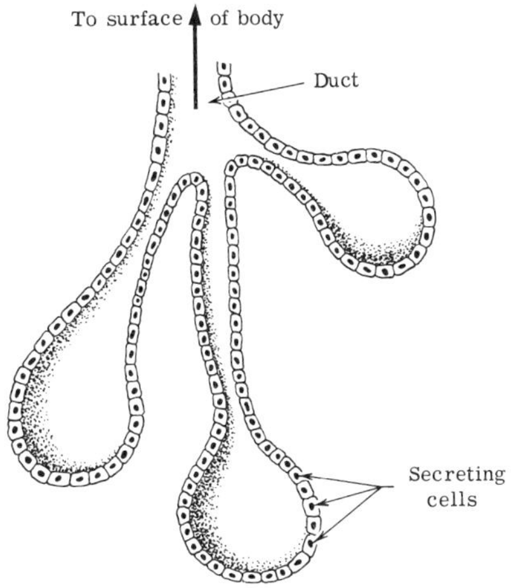

To surface ▲ of body

Duct

Secreting
cells

FIGURE 90

1845. A duct is a small tube. In Figure 90, note how the duct connects with the type of gland that we call

duct   a _____ gland.

1846. When the duct gland is activated to secrete its product, the product leaves the gland proper and

duct/tube   flows through the _____, shown at the top of Figure 90.

1847. The product is then carried from where it is

duct gland   generated in the _____ _____, through the duct to the SURFACE of the body.

1848. The sweat gland is an example of a duct gland. Sweat is manufactured in the sweat gland and trans-

surface   mitted through the attached duct to the _____ of the body.

sweat   1849. One example of a duct gland is the _____

gland   _____.

salivary

1850. The SALIVARY gland is another duct gland. SALIVA is manufactured in one type of duct gland, called the _____ gland, and is conducted through the attached duct into the mouth.

saliva

1851. Because the inside of the mouth is continuous with the outer skin of the body, we can consider it part of the surface of the body. Salivary glands secrete the product called _____ into the mouth.

duct

1852. Because it secretes its product to the surface of the body, the tear gland is another example of a _____ gland.

tear

1853. Tears are manufactured by the _____ gland. The tears are then carried through the tear duct of the lower eyelid into the eyes.

duct

1854. Ex derives from the Greek word meaning OUT OF, or OUTSIDE. Another name for _____ glands is EXOCRINE (ĕk'sō krīn) GLANDS.

exocrine

1855. Because they secrete their product out of, or to the outside of, the body, duct glands are also called _____ glands.

sweat/salivary
exocrine

1856. The tear gland and the _____ gland are examples of duct, or _____ glands.

exocrine

1857. Another name for duct glands is _____ glands.

exocrine
ductless

1858. The two types of glands are: 1) duct, or as they are also called, _____ glands, and 2) _____ glands.

not

1859. Duct glands have ducts that secrete their product to the surface of the body. Ductless glands, on the other hand, do _____ have ducts.

ductless glands

1860. Because they lack ducts, the second type of gland is called _____ _____.

exocrine

ductless

1861. Another name for duct glands is _____ glands, whereas an alternative name for _____ glands is ENDOCRINE glands.

endocrine

1862. We saw that the EX of exocrine derives from the Latin word meaning OUTSIDE. In like manner, the ENDO of _____ derives from the Greek word meaning WITHIN.

endocrine/ductless

1863. Whereas the exocrine glands secrete their product to the outside of the body, the _____ glands secrete their product within the body.

not

1864. The product of the endocrine glands is _____ secreted to the surface of the body.

ducts

1865. Endocrine glands lack _____, and secrete their product inside the body.

products

1866. Where, inside the body, do the endocrine glands secrete their _____?

endocrine

products

1867. The answer is that the _____ _____ glands secrete their _____ directly into the blood stream.

blood

1868. The endocrine glands do not have ducts, but rather, secrete their products directly into the _____ stream.

endocrine glands

1869. The blood stream can then distribute the products of the _____ _____ to a wide variety of places throughout the body.

products

1870. The blood vessels distribute blood throughout the body. Contained in the blood are the _____ secreted by the endocrine glands.

endocrine glands   1871. The products secreted by the _____ _____ are chemical compounds called HOR-MONES.

1872. Endocrine glands secrete chemical compounds
hormones   called _____.

hormones   1873. Chemical compounds called _____ are manufactured by the endocrine glands, and are
blood   secreted directly into the _____ stream.

hormones   1874. Once these _____ enter the
blood   _____ stream, they are widely distributed throughout the body.

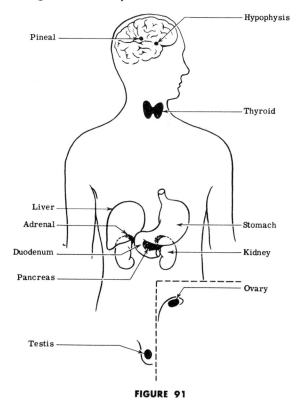

Pineal — Hypophysis

Thyroid

Liver — Adrenal — Stomach

Duodenum — Kidney

Pancreas — Ovary

Testis

FIGURE 91

1875. There are a number of different endocrine glands located in various places of the body. In Figure
endocrine glands   91, you see where the _____ _____ are located.

adrenal

1876. Note, for instance, the adrenal glands. We have already learned that the product secreted by the internal part of the _____ glands is called adrenalin.

adrenalin

1877. The name of the hormone manufactured by the internal part of the adrenal glands is _____.

adrenalin

1878. As we previously learned, one function of _____ is to cause the liver to release an increased amount of blood sugar.

adrenal glands

blood

1879. That is, the hormone adrenalin is manufactured by the _____ _____, then it is secreted into the blood stream, and carried by the _____ stream to the liver.

hormone

liver

1880. When the _____ called adrenalin reaches the liver, it causes the _____ to excrete an increased amount of blood sugar into the blood stream.

blood sugar

1881. This extra _____ _____ gives the person increased energy to respond in an emergency situation.

thyroid

1882. In Figure 91, observe the THYROID gland in the neck region. The hormone secreted by the _____ gland is called THYROXIN.

thyroxin

1883. The thyroid gland manufactures and secretes the hormone called _____ into the blood stream.

thyroxin

1884. Excesses and shortages of thyroxin in the blood stream have a number of interesting effects. For example, a shortage of _____ in the blood stream may result in a goiter.

thyroid

1885. A goiter is an enlargement of the _____ gland.

thyroxin

1886. What happens is this: When the thyroid gland is deficient, it does not produce enough _____.

thyroid

1887. Because the body demands more thyroxin than is produced by the _____ gland, the thyroid gland must compensate for this deficiency.

thyroxin
blood

1888. In order to compensate for a lack of _____ in the _____ stream, an enlargement takes place in the thyroid gland.

hormone

1889. That is, the thyroid gland, located in the neck, grows larger in order to produce an increased supply of the _____ called thyroxin.

neck

1890. As the thyroid gland grows in size, a bump or protrusion can be observed in the region of the _____.

thyroid

1891. This bump, or protrusion, indicates an enlargement of the _____ gland, and is called a goiter.

thyroxin

1892. A person with a deficient output of the thyroid gland has an under supply of _____ in the blood stream.

increase/
enlargement

1893. Because his body needs more thyroxin, an _____ in the size of the thyroid gland occurs.

thyroxin
blood

1894. The enlargement of the thyroid gland allows an increase in the amount of _____ to be secreted into the _____ stream.

goiter

1895. The increase in the size of the thyroid gland may be quite noticeable. When we see a bump, or protrusion, in the neck region of a person, we might suspect that the person has a _____.

adrenal; thyroid
(either order)

1896. We have now considered two endocrine glands: the ——————— and the ——————— glands.

endocrine

1897. As you can see in Figure 91, there are a number of other ——————— glands in the body.

hormone

1898. This brief consideration of two endocrine glands should give you a general idea of how they all function. That is, they all secrete their particular kind of product, or more specifically, their specific ——————— into the blood stream.

endocrine gland

1899. The particular hormone secreted by each ——————— ——————— has its own peculiar effect on some part of the body.

endocrine

1900. In your later work, you should explore the interesting story of how the various ——————— glands FUNCTION.

function

1901. For now, it is sufficient to have a GENERAL idea of how the endocrine glands ——————— to produce a response.

hormones

1902. That is, a response occurs when they secrete ——————— into the blood stream.

endocrine
response

1903. We have now considered the two general types of glands. When either an exocrine or an ——————— gland secretes its product, a ——————— occurs.

saliva

1904. For example, a response occurs when the salivary gland secretes ——————— into the mouth.

sweat; responses

1905. Similarly, when the tear gland secretes tears into the eyes, or when sweat is secreted by the ——————— glands, ——————— occur.

adrenalin
thyroxin

1906. Similarly, a response occurs when the adrenal glands secrete _____ into the blood stream, or when _____ is secreted by the thyroid gland.